# THE
# BALTIC COUNTRIES

## ESTONIA, LATVIA, and LITHUANIA

BY ADRIANE RUGGIERO

**DILLON PRESS**
**PARSIPPANY, NEW JERSEY**

*For my mother*

## Acknowledgments

The author wishes to thank the following individuals: Ilse Berzins for sharing her memories, Leelo Lass of the Estonian Embassy and Liana Eglitis of the Latvian Embassy for providing information about education in their respective countries, Tina Pelikan of ECM for providing music and biographical information about Baltic composers, and Vello Pettai for reviewing the manuscript and giving helpful suggestions.

In Chapter 7, the section entitled "An Age-Old Craft" is adapted from the article "Messages in Mittens: The Story of a Latvian Knitter" by Sandra Messinger. The article originally appeared in the November/December 1995 issue of *PieceWork*, published by Interweave Press, Inc., Loveland, CO. Used by permission.

Page 92: "Vilna" by Moyshe Kulbak. From *A Treasury of Yiddish Poetry* by Irving Howe and Eliezer Greenberg, editors, © 1969 by Irving Howe and Eliezer Greenberg. Reprinted by permission of Henry Holt & Co., Inc.

### Photo Credits

Front cover: *l.* Serge Attal/Sygma Photo News; *m.* Pascal Le Segretain/Sygma Photo News; *r.* Sovfoto/Eastfoto.

Allsport USA: 122; Rick Stewart: 121. American Museum of Natural History: 27. Vytautas Bazikas: 33, 36, 48. Joe Coca: 112. Comstock/Sven Martson: 64. Mary Evans Picture Library: 21, 40, 53. FPG International/Earl Young: 23. Jeff Greenberg: 6, 13, 52, 78, 79, 85, 92, 98, 101, 124, 126. New York Public Library: 107. Adriane Ruggiero: 46, 144. Silver Burdett Ginn: 7, 11, 14. Sovfoto/Eastfoto: 22, 24, 50, 70, 82, 96, 110, 116, 118, 128; ITAR-TASS: 56, 59, 73. Sygma Photo News: 74, 90, 131; Serge Attal: 76, 119; C. Langridge/Baltic States: 25; Pascal Le Segretain: 10; A. Nogues: 72. Map, Ortelius Design: 16.

### Library of Congress Cataloging-in-Publication Data

Ruggiero, Adriane.
    The Baltic countries—Estonia, Latvia, and Lithuania / by Adriane Ruggiero. — 1st ed.
        p. cm. — (Discovering our heritage)
    Summary: Describes the people, culture, geography, history, and customs of Estonia, Latvia, and Lithuania while emphasizing the national pride of these countries no longer dominated by the former Soviet Union.
    Includes bibliographical references and index.
    ISBN 0-382-39472-0 (lsb).
    1. Baltic States—Juvenile literature. [1. Baltic States.]
    I. Title. II. Series.
    DK502.35.R84  1998                          96-41447
    947'.4—dc20

Published by Dillon Press
A Division of Simon & Schuster
299 Jefferson Road, Parsippany, NJ 07054

First edition
Printed in the United States of America
10 9 8 7 6 5 4 3 2 1

# CONTENTS

# Preface

When he was awarded the Nobel Prize for literature in 1980, the Lithuanian-born poet and writer Czeslaw Milosz said this of his boyhood home: "It is good to be born in a small country where nature is on a human scale, where various languages and religions have coexisted for centuries." The subject of this book is the countries of the Baltic: Estonia, Latvia, and Lithuania. Although they are small, their history and culture are as complex as any country's in Europe. Today the countries of the Baltic have emerged from years of foreign domination as free and independent nations. They stand between Eastern and Western Europe, independent but also dependent, needing their neighbors and other countries of the world for aid and trade.

By getting to know the peoples of the Baltic, and their history and culture, we can begin to understand some of the complexities of Europe's past. As we try to understand that past, we can begin to appreciate the challenges facing the Baltic peoples as they try to create a place for themselves within the Europe of today.

# Fast Facts About Estonia

**Official Name:**  Republic of Estonia (*Eesti Vabariik*)

**Capital:**  Tallinn

**Location:**  The most northern of the three Baltic countries, Estonia is located on the east coast of the Baltic Sea. To the north of Estonia is the Gulf of Finland. Latvia is to the south, Russia to the east, and the Baltic Sea on the west.

**Area:**  Estonia is about 17,400 square miles (45,100 square kilometers) in area, about the same size as New Hampshire and Vermont combined. It is larger than Denmark or the Netherlands, two other countries of northern Europe. Estonia has a sweeping 481-mile (774-kilometer) coastline.

**Elevation:**  Estonia is part of a low-lying plain that is itself part of the vast North European Plain. The average elevation in Estonia is 164 feet (50 meters) above sea level. The highest point in Estonia, also the highest point in the Baltic region, is Sur Munamägi (Great Egg Hill), with an elevation of a little more than 1,043 feet (318 meters). The lowest-lying areas of Estonia are along the western coast.

**Population:**  Estonia has a little over 1.6 million people. About 72 percent of Estonians live in or near cities. Nearly one third of the total population lives in or around the capital, Tallinn. In 1995, Tallinn had a population of about 485,000.

*A view of Tallinn, Estonia*

**Form of Government:** In 1992, Estonia declared itself a constitutional republic in which the people vote for officials to represent them in the country's parliament. Called the Riigikogu, this lawmaking body has 101 members, elected to four-year terms. The Estonian president is elected by the Riigikogu. According to the 1992 constitution, the powers of the president are limited. The prime minister is the chief executive of the government and is nominated by the president.

**National Flag:** A tricolor of three horizontal stripes. The colors of the flag are blue, black, and white.

**National Anthem:** "My Native Land, My Pride and Joy"

**Basic Unit of Money:** The *kroon*. In 1997, 12 kroons equaled approximately 1 United States dollar.

**Major Languages:** Most Estonians speak Estonian, a language closely related to Finnish, the language of Finland. City dwellers often also speak English and Finnish. Russian is spoken by ethnic Russians who live in Estonia and also by some older Estonians who learned the language during the years of Soviet rule. However, Estonians today feel strongly about speaking their own language. They proudly regard their language as a symbol of independence.

**Major Religions:** Under Soviet rule the practice of religion in Estonia was suppressed. With independence, Estonians became free to worship as they pleased. There are Lutheran churches in Estonia as well as Catholic, Eastern Orthodox, and Jewish congregations.

**Major Holidays:** January 1—New Year's Day; February 24—Independence Day, in celebration of Estonia's first secession from Russia, 1918; Good Friday; May 1; March 25 and June 14—commemorating the deportation of Baltic peoples to Siberia during the years of Soviet rule; June 23—Victory Day, battle of Võnnu, 1919; June 24—Jaanipäev (St. John's Day); November 16—Rebirth Day, in celebration of Estonia's Declaration of Sovereignty, 1988; December 25—Christmas Day; December 26—the day after Christmas

# Fast Facts About Latvia

**Official Name:** Republic of Latvia (*Latvijas Republika*)

**Capital:** Riga

**Location:** The middle of the three Baltic states, Latvia is located on the eastern coast of the Baltic Sea. Estonia is to the north, Lithuania to the south, and Russia and Belarus to the east. The twenty-fifth meridian—the east-west divide of Europe—runs through the center of Latvia.

**Area:** Latvia is about 24,600 square miles (63,700 square kilometers) in area, roughly the size of West Virginia. It is larger than Switzerland and Denmark. The western part of the country is dominated by a smooth 293-mile-long (472-kilometer-long) coastline that swings around the Gulf of Riga and includes beaches and dunes along the Baltic Sea.

**Elevation:** Like Estonia, most of Latvia is a low-lying plain. The countryside consists of rolling plains, forests, marshes, and gentle hills. The average elevation is about 292 feet (89 meters) above sea level. Dunes along the Baltic coast can reach a height of 125 feet (38 meters) above sea level. The highest point in Latvia—1,025-foot (312-meter) Gaizinkalns—is located in the center of the country.

**Population:** Latvia has about 2.5 million people, 52 percent of whom are Letts, the official nationality of Latvia. Russians represent 34 percent of the population.

*A young Latvian girl in national costume*

About 71 percent of the population lives in and around cities. About one third of the people live in the capital and port city of Riga.

**Form of Government:** Latvia is a republic whose constitution dates from 1922. The constitution is the country's supreme law. The country is headed by a president, who answers to the Saeima, Latvia's parliament, or lawmaking body. This 100-member legislature confirms government decrees and approves the heads of government offices named by the president.

**National Flag:** Two broad horizontal stripes and one narrow horizontal stripe. The colors are dark red and white.

**National Anthem:** "God Bless Latvia"

**Basic Unit of Money:** The *lats* (plural, *lati*). In 1997, 0.57 lats equaled approximately 1 United States dollar.

**Major Languages:** Latvian is the official language of the country, and a speaking knowledge of it is necessary for citizenship. Young Latvians also study English, German, and French. Russians who live in Latvia continue to speak their language.

**Major Religions:** Religious freedom is guaranteed under Latvia's constitution. The Lutheran Church is the largest organized religion in Latvia. There are also Catholic, Russian Orthodox, Baptist, and Jewish congregations.

**Major Holidays:** January 1—New Year's Day; Good Friday; May 1—Labor Day; June 24—Jāni (St. John's Day); November 18—National Day; December 25—Christmas Day; Latvia also commemorates March 25 and June 14. On these dates, Latvians recall the deportation of Baltic peoples to Siberia during the years of Soviet rule.

## Fast Facts About Lithuania

**Official Name:**    Republic of Lithuania (*Lietuvos Respublika*)

**Capital:** Vilnius

**Location:** The largest of the Baltic countries, Lithuania is bounded by Latvia on the north, Belarus on the east and south, Poland on the southwest, Kaliningrad (a division of Russia) also on the southwest, and the Baltic Sea on the west.

**Area:** Lithuania has an area of 25,175 square miles (65,200 square kilometers) and is twice the size of Belgium. It is situated at approximately the same latitude as southern Canada, and its longitude places it almost at the center of the European continent. Lithuania's Baltic coastline extends for about 60 miles (96 km) along sandy beaches and high dunes.

**Elevation:** Like its neighbors Latvia and Estonia, Lithuania is part of the North European Plain. Gentle hills in the west and south emerge from a mainly level landscape. The entire country is less than 961 feet (293 meters) above sea level.

**Population:** Lithuania's population is approximately 3.7 million, with about 70 percent of the people living in and around cities. Vilnius is the capital and largest city, with a population of 600,000. Lithuanians make up more than 80 percent of the population. Russians

*The city of Vilnius on the Neris River*

comprise about 9 percent of the population, and Poles 7 percent. There are also Ukrainians, Belarusians, and Jews in Lithuania.

**Form of Government:** Lithuania's new constitution came into being in 1992. The Seimas, or parliament, is the

highest lawmaking body in the country. It has 141 members, elected to four-year terms. The president is the head of state and is elected to a five-year term. The president appoints a prime minister with the approval of parliament.

**National Flag:** A tricolor of three horizontal stripes of gold, green, and red.

**National Anthem:** "Lithuania, Land of Heroes"

**Basic Unit of Money:** The *litas*. In 1995 four litas were worth about one United States dollar.

**Major Languages:** Lithuanian is the official language of the country. Other languages, however, are spoken and understood in Lithuania. Russian is spoken and understood as a result of the years of Soviet rule. German is also spoken, as are English and Polish.

**Major Religions:** The Roman Catholic Church is the largest organized faith in Lithuania, and most Lithuanians are Catholics. Before World War II, around 200,000 Jews lived in Lithuania. Ninety-five percent died in Nazi concentration camps. Today religious freedom is guaranteed by Lithuania's constitution.

**Major Holidays:** January 1—New Year's Day; February 16—Independence Day, in celebration of the restoration of Lithuanian statehood, 1918; Easter; First Sunday in May—Mother's Day; July 6—Statehood Day, in celebration of the crowning of King Mindaugas and the foundation of the Lithuanian state; November 1—All Saints' Day; December 25—Christmas Day

# AT THE CENTER OF EUROPE

Estonia, Latvia, and Lithuania make up a region of northeastern Europe known as the Baltic. The Baltic is just a small corner of the European continent. In fact, the combined land area of Estonia, Latvia, and Lithuania is less than that of Great Britain. Facing the Scandinavian peninsula across the Baltic Sea and backed by the vast Russian landmass, the countries of the Baltic form a borderland between Western and Eastern Europe. This location has both helped and hurt the Baltic countries.

Located at the geographic center of Europe—on the twenty-fifth meridian, the east-west dividing line of the continent—the Baltic is a place where diverse cultures, nationalities, languages, goods, and ideas have met and mixed over the centuries. The main physical features of the region, a long coastline and level plains, have always made the Baltic lands vulnerable to invasion. At various times, Germans, Swedes, Danes, Poles, and Russians invaded, claimed, and divided up the lands of the Baltic and subdued the peoples who lived there. Their territory seized, their native languages suppressed, and their traditions and history erased because they were considered inferior, the peoples of the Baltic frequently joined the ranks of other European peoples without countries to call their own.

The Baltics did achieve statehood in the years following World War I (1914–1918), only to lose it in World War II (1939–1945). In 1940, Estonia, Latvia, and Lithuania were swallowed up by the Soviet Union and disappeared from the map of European nations. They became republics of the Union of Soviet Socialist Republics. The peoples of the Baltic nearly disappeared, too, as the Soviets deported and executed them and tried to extinguish their culture in many ways. Westerners were not allowed to travel freely in the Baltics or other Soviet republics and therefore knew little or nothing about the "disappeared" countries. Questions about Estonia, Latvia, and Lithuania were answered with shrugs of ignorance. Many people around the world did not know the difference between the Baltic countries and the Balkans, a group of countries in southeastern Europe. Worse still, they could not have cared less.

Events in the late twentieth century brought about tremendous changes in Europe, however. The Soviet Union fell apart and one after another its 15 republics declared their independence. Like the other republics, the Baltic countries emerged from the long, dark period of Soviet domination to become independent states anxious to take their place among Europe's community of nations. Today each has its own government, currency, language, and culture. All three face huge problems caused by years of Soviet misrule. There is no guarantee that the Baltic countries will succeed in changing from closed, Communist societies to open, democratic societies. One thing is certain, though. The people of the Baltic countries are proud to call themselves Estonians, Latvians, and Lithuanians and want the world to know about them and their long, eventful past.

## Bounded by the Sea

Although each Baltic country has its own history, language, and culture, the three nations share location. When you look at the Baltic countries on a map, the first thing you see is a hook-shaped coastline. From Estonia in the north to Lithuania in the south, the Baltic countries border the shallow, placid body of water called the Baltic Sea. The Baltic is an arm of the Atlantic Ocean and flows into two smaller gulfs. The Gulf of Bothnia washes along the shores of Sweden and Finland. The narrow Gulf of Finland separates southern Finland and northern Estonia. The shank of the coastal hook is bordered by the large Gulf of Riga, with the western region of Latvia forming the tip of the hook. To the west of the widest part of the Baltic Sea is the southern coast of Sweden and the Danish peninsula. Beyond Denmark is the North Sea, and beyond that, the stormy Atlantic Ocean. Other countries bordering the

Baltic Sea are Russia, Poland, and Germany.

In prehistoric times, when the earth's surface was still taking shape, the Baltic Sea was a freshwater lake. Around 2000 B.C., the small waterways around Denmark known as the Danish straits opened up, and the salty water of the North Sea flowed in. Even today, however, the Baltic is less salty than the North Sea, largely because of the many freshwater rivers that flow into it.

Water has played an important role in the history of the Baltic countries from earliest times. For centuries the peoples of the Baltic have traded goods and ideas across and up and down the body of water that gives the region its name. They sailed across the sea and along its coasts in search of adventure, new lands to settle, and goods to trade. Merchants and shipbuilders took advantage of the ice-free ports of the Baltic to trade with the rest of Europe.

Of all the nations of the Baltic, Latvia's history is the most closely tied to the sea. Riga, Latvia's capital and largest city, was a major port and trading center in medieval times. Riga's stout ships carried amber, furs, fish, cut trees, and metal tools and weapons from places deep inland to ports in Germany, Sweden, and England.

Latvian fishers made their living from the sea, hauling in herring. Estonia also has a long seafaring history. First conquered by the Danes and then by the Germans, the Estonian city of Tallinn became an important trading center

*This illustration shows Riga's waterfront around 1550.*

during the 1300s and 1400s. Traders exchanged animal furs, honey, and other goods for wine, fish, cloth, and salt and shipped these east into neighboring Russia and south to the Black Sea. From the city of Constantinople (present-day Istanbul), goods traveled into Asia and farther south to the Middle East. After many wars in which it was conquered and reconquered by foreign armies, Tallinn became an important port in the Russian empire in the 1800s.

Although its coastline is shorter, Lithuania has its own major seaport and city, Klaipėda. Founded by Germans in

*Fishing is still an important industry in Estonia.*

the 1200s, Klaipėda was known by its German name of Memel for many years. It was a shipbuilding center during the 1700s and 1800s.

## An Easy Landscape

The Baltic countries sit on the westernmost part of the North European Plain, a region of mainly flat expanses and gently rolling hills. The Estonian, Latvian, and Lithuanian landscape also features extensive forests, sandy beaches, numerous inlets and bays, large and small islands, and dense marshlands. These formations are the result of the

*Bales of hay dot this level landscape in Estonia.*

action of huge glaciers, which gouged out the earth as they melted and shrank during prehistoric times. Several ice ages helped create northern Europe's rich, fertile soil as well as the hundreds of rivers, streams, and lakes across the land. The two largest rivers in the Baltic are the Daugava, which empties into the Gulf of Riga in Latvia, and the Nemunas, which flows through southwestern Lithuania and empties into the Courland Lagoon. The lagoon is a small body of water separated from the larger Baltic Sea by a long thin finger of land called the Courland Spit. Other major rivers are the Narva, which flows from 60-mile-long (96-kilometer-long) Lake Peipus, on the border between

*Lake Engura in Latvia*

Estonia and Russia, into the Gulf of Finland, and the Gauja, which flows completely within eastern Latvia.

The coastland of Estonia, Latvia, and Lithuania is different from the rest of the countryside. The gray-blue waters of the Baltic crash up on wide beaches that stretch for miles into the distance. Tall dunes give way to birch and pine forests. The air of the Baltic coast is filled with the smell of salt water and the scent of the pine forests. This is the Amber Coast, a part of the Baltic famous for amber deposits.

*The Baltic's wide beaches stretch for miles.*

## The Baltic's Golden Treasure

Golden-brown in color or sometimes even orange, red, green, or blue, amber is unlike any other substance on Earth. Sometimes it is called a mineral or a semiprecious stone. In fact, amber is the remains of ancient tree resin. Preserved inside amber in a kind of miniature museum are insects, flowers, seeds, bits of leaves, and other once-living things. How they were preserved in this way is an amazing story of nature at work.

Trees with cones and some broad-leaved trees produce soft, gooey resin that protects the trees from insects. As insects eat into a tree's wood and cause a branch or limb to fall off, resin rises to the surface, sealing off the wound and preventing further harm. When insects stay on the tree too long, they get stuck in the oozing resin and remain trapped when it becomes hard. When the tree dies and falls to the ground, it may take hundreds of years for it to break up and become part of the soil. As the process of disintegration takes place, the resin survives and is deposited in bogs and marshlands or is washed away by rushing rivers.

Today, amber deposits are found in such far-flung areas of the world as Lebanon, the Dominican Republic, and New Jersey. The most famous examples of amber, however, are underneath the Baltic seabed in deposits that date to nearly 40 million years ago. The Baltic Sea contains the world's largest amber deposit. When jagged chunks of ice rip through the shallow Baltic, they scrape up pieces of the amber left in the seabed long ago. Winter storms toss the cloudy stones up on the beaches, where fishers and beachcombers collect them. Once polished, amber reveals its golden beauty and much more. Inside, tiny insect wings thousands of years old or sometimes even a fully formed flower can be seen.

Amber has been valued for its rich color from ancient times. Stone Age peoples in northern Europe carved

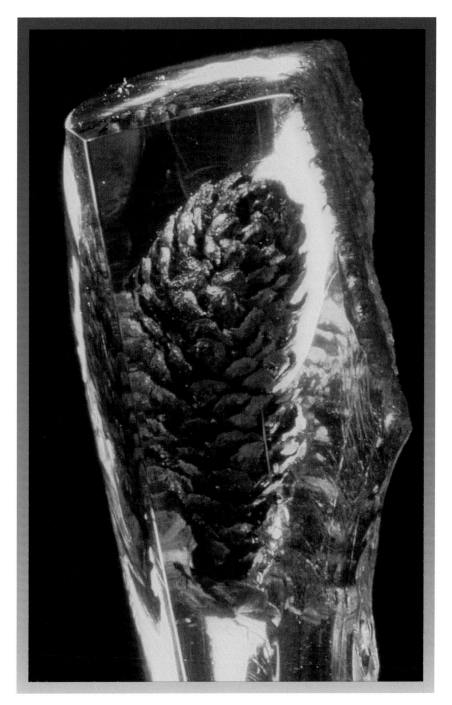

*An ancient pine cone preserved within a peice of amber*

chunks of Baltic amber into animal-shaped figures that they used during religious rites. Known to early peoples long before gold, amber became an important trade item in and beyond the Baltic. Amber pieces, either raw stones or polished pieces carved into jewelry and ornaments, were carried far and wide across the ancient world. Pieces of amber have been discovered in the tombs of Egyptian pharaohs. Well-to-do women of ancient Rome wore amber earrings, rings, and necklaces.

In the 1700s, Russia's ruler Peter the Great preserved a gift of amber from a fellow monarch in a special way. Peter used the pieces of amber as a wallcovering for a room in one of his palaces. A visitor to the palace described the room as "a jewel box." The Amber Room endured as a symbol of the fabulous wealth of Russia's czars until German armies invaded Russia during World War II. The fate of the unusual treasure is a mystery. It is not known whether it was broken into pieces by German troops or was destroyed in bombings. Although the Amber Room is now only a memory, present-day visitors to the Baltic can find their own small treasures in the form of beautiful amber necklaces, pins, rings, and insect-filled stones.

Today, amber is considered more valuable than ever, for reasons other than its beauty. Scientists can recover DNA, the genetic identity of all living matter, from the insects preserved inside the amber. After studying the

DNA, scientists can make conclusions about the insects' history and evolution.

## Deep, Mysterious Forests

The amber-rich coast of the Baltic has played an important role in the region's geography and history, but forests are even more important to the peoples of the Baltic. Before people began to farm the land, forests covered much of the Baltic region. Scientists believe that forests covered almost 85 percent of the land in Latvia in ancient times. Today, forests make up just over 25 percent of Latvia. In Estonia, however, forests cover almost 40 percent of the land. Much of the Baltic forests were cut for timber for use in shipbuilding and house construction. Logging is still a major industry in the Baltic, and Baltic pine is widely sought after.

Despite the large-scale lumbering in the region, Estonia, Latvia, and Lithuania still have dense forests of ancient pine, oak, birch, and spruce. The oldest oak tree in Europe, the Stelmuze oak, is located in Lithuania. It measures almost 40 feet (12 meters) around and is said to be at least 1,500 years old! The forests are also habitats for many kinds of wildlife. The animals of the forest were routinely hunted until the early 1900s by nobles who owned vast Baltic estates and used the forests as their private hunting grounds. Wild animals such as elk, boar, deer, wolves, bear, and lynx still make their home in heavily wooded areas and nature preserves.

Legends and folk tales about forests are widespread in the Baltic. The earliest peoples of the region worshiped the oak tree and believed in forest spirits and gods. Stories about flesh-eating wolves, ferocious bears, and dog-headed people were known by all. Besides being dark and mysterious places, forests were also good places to hide from invading armies. Many times in their history, Baltic peoples fled to the forests to hide from their enemies. They also used the forests as a place to organize resistance to conquerors. The Baltic peoples' bond with forests is still strong, though less desperate and scary than in the past. A favorite pastime of many in the Baltic is taking a quiet walk through the forests and fields to gather mushrooms or berries or just to enjoy the beauty of the land.

## A Mild Northern Climate

Most of the Baltic region enjoys a temperate climate. Temperatures near the coast tend to be moderate all year long because of the warm currents that flow from the Gulf of Mexico northward into the Atlantic Ocean and on to the Baltic Sea. Summer temperatures rarely rise above 80° Fahrenheit (27° Celsius), with July and August the warmest and rainiest months. During the long winter—November through March—temperatures rarely fall below 16° Fahrenheit (-9° Celsius).

As one moves inland however, the warming effects of the Gulf Stream lessen, and temperatures become more extreme. The climate of the North European Plain takes over in the interior. Summers are warmer and winters are colder than on the coast, with heavy snowfalls and subzero temperatures. Lakes and marshes in the interior freeze during the long winters. Sometimes the Gulf of Finland and the Gulf of Riga freeze over, too. The open Baltic Sea, however, almost never freezes, allowing ferries and ships to travel back and forth all year between the Baltic, Swedish, and Finnish coasts.

Like their Scandinavian neighbors to the west, the Baltic countries are located in the northern latitudes of the Northern Hemisphere. During the winter months this part of Earth is tilted far away from the sun. Days are short, with very few hours of sunlight. Sometimes the sky seems to hardly brighten at all. In deepest winter the sun hangs very low in the heavens. Families rise to get ready for work or school while it is still dark outside. The sky begins to lighten at around nine o'clock in the morning, and by four in the afternoon it is already dark.

Although Baltic winters can be dark and gloomy, the people of the region adapt by using that time of year to attend concerts, plays, and opera and ballet performances. They also enjoy quiet times at home, reading, knitting, listening to music, and watching favorite television shows. During the brief daylight hours, young and old enjoy ice-skating on frozen lakes and ponds and cross-country skiing through fields and forests. Thoughts of summer are never far away, though.

The summer months are a special time in the Baltic. As the Northern Hemisphere tilts toward the sun, the days begin to grow longer. Storks start to return in April, a sure sign of spring. Their rooftop nests are a symbol of good luck. By June the days are quite long. At this time of year, some areas of northern Estonia enjoy 19 hours of daylight! The people of the Baltic savor the almost continual daylight by staying outdoors as much as possible. Picnicking, sailing, swimming, and hiking are enjoyed by all. Summer is also the time to sunbathe on the sandy beaches along the Baltic coast or walk in the mushroom-carpeted forests. Those who own summer homes or cottages flock to them to rest or do gardening or light farming. Nature lovers can observe the many different kinds of birds and animals that make their homes in the Baltic woodlands and along the region's many waterways.

*A young stork sits in its treetop nest.*

# EARLY HISTORY

People began to settle in the countries we call Estonia, Latvia, and Lithuania from about 9000 B.C. to about 7500 B.C. One group—the ancestors of present-day Estonians—first appeared on the shores of the Baltic Sea almost 2,500 years before the birth of Christ. They were part of a larger group of people who spread out over the forests of northern Russia and spoke a language related to Finnish. The ancient Roman historian Tacitus called them "Aesti," a name that makes up part of the official name of Estonia today.

Another group of settlers—the ancestors of present-day Latvians and Lithuanians—arrived in the Baltic 2,000 to 1,500 years before the birth of Christ. They spoke a language whose roots can be traced to Sanskrit and Persian, languages spoken in present-day India and Iran. To see the similarities between Lithuanian and Sanskrit, compare the Lithuanian and Sanskrit words for "god," "day," and "son." In Lithuanian these words are *dievas, diena*, and *sunus*. In Sanskrit they are *devas, dina*, and *sunu*. Did the earliest Latvians and Lithuanians come from Asia? No one knows for certain, but scientists do know that early peoples traveled over greater distances than originally thought. Their languages evolved as they traveled. By 2000 B.C., groups of people had settled around the eastern shore of the Baltic Sea and began to farm the land there.

There were no Baltic nations in ancient times. Instead, the earliest Baltic peoples were organized in tribes united by language and kinship. These tribes included the Estonians in the north, the Livs in what became Latvia, the Samogitians in the future Lithuania, and the Prussians to the southwest, along the border with present-day Poland and Germany. Baltic peoples living in the eastern part of the region gradually merged with the Slavs of Russia. The Baltic tribes lived in a small area, in fortified settlements under the leadership of elders. The people fished, hunted, and worshiped their gods. Most of the gods were believed to live in nature, especially in the forests.

## Ancient Beliefs

The early Baltic peoples were pagans who believed in many gods. The ancient deities worshiped by these people were thought to live everywhere in nature: in rivers, forests, lakes, marshlands, and meadows. Even the sea was home to gods and goddesses. Oak trees were especially sacred to the ancient Balts, but all of nature was a part of human existence and was respected and honored.

The three most important gods in ancient Latvia and Lithuania were Dievs, Mara, and Laima. Dievs was the sky god and lived on a mountaintop. In charge of the universe,

*In Lithuania, large wooden sculptures often show ancient dieties.*

Dievs was similar to a tribal elder and helped people in their everyday lives. Mara was the goddess of the earth and was responsible for all living things. Mara is often pictured in Latvian artwork and has become the symbol of Latvian freedom. Laima was the god of fate, who decided the destiny of all newborn children. Other deities were Saule, the sun goddess; Perkons, the god of thunder; and Jumis, the god of eternal life. There was also a goddess of the forest and numerous lesser gods and goddesses, all of whom ruled over aspects of human life. Many people in the Baltic today preserve elements of the traditional beliefs as a reminder of their history. They blend pagan rites with Christian beliefs in many of their festivals and feasts.

## Contacts With the Outside World

The early Baltic peoples took advantage of their location on the sea and near rivers to establish trading networks with neighbors to the north, south, east, and west. One of their trade items was amber, the honey-colored stone from the Baltic seabed. Other products they traded included grain, flax, metalwork, and animal furs. By the A.D. 400s, the peoples of the Baltic and their trade goods were well-known throughout northeastern Europe and as far south as the Mediterranean Sea. Baltic peoples prospered from their trade with the Roman Empire. With the wealth they accumulated from trade, they expanded their areas of control eastward into what became Russia.

By the 600s, Balts had begun to come under attack as neighboring peoples moved into their lands. In the west, Vikings from Scandinavia raided Baltic coastal settlements. The Viking trade route to Russia and Ukraine during the 700s and 800s was along the Daugava River, Latvia's main waterway. Warfare between the Balts and the Vikings continued until the 1200s. There was also pressure from the east. Slavs pushed into Baltic lands in the 1000s and 1100s in an attempt to conquer the pagan peoples there and convert them to Orthodox Christianity. Eventually the Baltic peoples retreated to their wooden settlements and earthen forts around the Baltic Sea. But their contact with the outside world continued.

## Conquest and Rule by German Knights

Most people in medieval Europe were Christians. Certain Christian rulers felt it was their duty to convert the neighboring Balts to Christianity, and they sent out missionaries to the pagans. German missionaries first appeared in Latvia in the early 1200s and established churches. The first German fort was built in Riga in 1201 by a German bishop who also set up an order of crusading knights to carry out the conversions. The Knights of the

Sword (known as the Livonian Knights after 1237) wore white robes covered with crosses and swords. These garments identified them as crusaders with a holy mission. The knights' swords and crossbows were more powerful than any weapons the Balts had, and in a few years the crusaders carved out their own country of Livonia (named after the original inhabitants, the Liv people) from territory around the Gulf of Riga. The Knights of the Sword ruled over the Livs, Estonians, and Latvians who lived in Livonia and forced them to accept Christianity. By the 1300s the peoples of the Baltic had been conquered and forcibly converted by the crusading knights.

The native peoples of the Baltic did not willingly accept the new faith or their new masters. Time and time again they rose up in revolt against German, Danish, Swedish, and Russian conquerors. The last great revolt of the Baltic peoples took place between 1343 and 1345, when Estonian warriors fought the Danes and killed several hundred of them. The Estonians were eventually defeated.

In the 1220s another group of German crusaders invaded the area. The Knights of the Teutonic Order were founded in Palestine in 1190 to fight the Muslims. Over the years the order became more concerned with military conquest in Europe and turned its quest for glory and power there. The Teutonic Knights found good opportunities to

*The Knights of the Teutonic Order conquered lands in the Baltic in the 1200s and 1300s.*

conquer new lands in the Baltic. When a German ruler invited the knights to wage war on his pagan neighbors, the Teutonic Knights had their chance. All through the 1200s the Teutonic Knights fought the Prussians, a people living along the southeastern shore of the Baltic, and brought Prussian lands under their control. By 1346 the Baltic coast from west of present-day Gdańsk, Poland, north to Narva, in northeastern Estonia, was under German control.

German rule in the Baltic was based on the feudal system. Under this system a prince or bishop held all the land and parceled it out to nobles in return for their support in wartime. The nobles became vassals of the prince or bishop and ruled over their holdings (called fiefs) from a castle or manor house. Serfs—peasants tied to the estate—worked the land for the noble, or lord. All crops and animals raised on the estate belonged to him.

Under the Germans the Baltic was divided into several fiefdoms. One was headed by the Teutonic Knights, another by the Livonian Knights, and a third by the archbishop of Riga. Other fiefdoms were headed by the bishops of Tallinn, Courland, and Tartu. The people of Estonia and Latvia became serfs on the estates of the German nobles.

German traders and merchants also influenced life in the Baltic. In the mid-1300s they set up a trading network throughout northern Germany and the Baltic. The network was called the Hanseatic League, from the word *Hanse* meaning "guild" or "merchants' association." The aim of this network of cities and trading posts was control of the fish and grain trade in northern Europe. Hanseatic merchants established colonies from Novgorod, in northwestern Russia, to Bruges, London, and even Venice. Their ships carried dried and salted fish to Prague and supplied grain from Riga to England and France. Riga, Tallinn, and other Baltic cities were members of the Hanseatic League and soon became rich through trade between Russia and the countries of western Europe. The merchants and tradespeople of the Hanseatic cities of the Baltic built fine houses and workshops to show off their prosperity and skill. By the 1500s the Baltic Sea had become one of the most important trading routes of Europe. On the northern coasts lay the Scandinavian nations of Sweden, Norway, and Denmark. On the southern side lay the holdings of the Teutonic Knights. South of this region was a vast land known as Lithuania.

## Lithuanian Lords

Unlike its neighbors Latvia and Estonia, medieval Lithuania had not come under German control. During their conquest of East Prussia, the Teutonic Knights did attack Lithuanian forts in an attempt to convert the pagan Lithuanians to Christianity, but pressure from this foreign army led the Lithuanian clans to unite in their own defense. By the mid-1200s the warrior Mindaugas had become the most powerful Lithuanian lord, and a Lithuanian state began to form around him. Mindaugas established alliances with rival clans and even became a Christian in the hope of fending off attacks by the Teutonic Knights. His conversion angered other Lithuanian lords, however. Mindaugas is believed to have been killed by pagan Lithuanian lords in 1263, and the Christian kingdom he created came to an end.

When the Mongols invaded eastern Europe in the 1230s, eastern Slavs sought Lithuanian protection from the invaders. As a result of granting protection to the Slavs, Lithuanian lords became rulers over much Slav territory. During this time the Lithuanians remained pagans, in sharp contrast to their Christian Slavic subjects. The Lithuanians were able to rule over the Slavs by means of their military might, their wealth from trade, and their ability to organize the lands under their control.

Lithuania became a power in northern Europe in the mid-1300s under the rule of Gediminas (1316–1341). Gediminas founded the city of Vilnius, on the Neris River. According to legend, Gediminas had a dream of an iron wolf fiercely howling from a hill near the Neris. When he awoke, Gediminas vowed to build a castle on a hilly spot in his camp. The castle would be strong enough to withstand the force of 100 wolves. It was there that the city of Vilnius was founded. Gediminas took advantage of the decline of Russia (centered in Kiev at the time) to push the borders of Lithuania eastward and southward into present-day Belarus and Ukraine. At this time, Lithuania was organized into districts, each of which was ruled by a governor. The districts were grouped into counties that were ruled from a castle held by the Grand Duke, the name given to the ruler of

Lithuania. All lands were held for the Grand Duke, who could divide his realm, called the Grand Duchy of Lithuania, among his sons.

Gediminas invited priests, traders, and landowners from around the Baltic to settle in Lithuania. A convert to Christianity, Gediminas sought help from the pope in settling a long period of warfare with the Teutonic Knights. Despite his strong leadership, Gediminas was unable to convince his fellow Lithuanians to accept Christianity. Nor was he able to hold back attacks by the Teutonic Knights. When Gediminas died, his lands were divided among two of his sons. One son, Algirdas, became ruler of Vilnius. Under the skilled leadership of Algirdas, Lithuania expanded eastward into Slav lands as never before. Parts of present-day Belarus and Ukraine were annexed in the mid-1300s. Western Russian lands were also taken by Lithuania at the same time. The Teutonic Knights continued to harass Lithuania in the late 1300s. When conquest failed, the determined knights ravaged the land and tried to lure unhappy Lithuanian princes to their side. War against the Teutonic Knights continued under Algirdas's son, Jogaila, or Jagiello (1378–1401).

## A Historic Union

By the 1300s the Lithuanians were the only Baltic

people who were still independent. They were ferocious pagan warriors who made human sacrifices to their thunder god, Perkunas. The Lithuanian lords were more tolerant than some of the Christian kings of Europe who held them in contempt, however. All religions—Christianity, Islam, and Judaism—were recognized and allowed to exist in Lithuania. In addition, the Lithuanians were unified against the Teutonic Knights and Russia. Nevertheless, the Grand Duke of Lithuania, Jogaila, was ever watchful against his enemies and sought allies to join with Lithuania. One possible ally was Poland, located to the south of Lithuanian lands. The Poles were also vulnerable to Teutonic attacks and needed a strong neighbor to help them defend themselves against the Germans. The only hindrance to a possible union between the two was religion. Poland was a Christian kingdom and would never welcome a pagan duke as ruler.

The Christian princes of Europe saw the value of a Polish-Lithuanian alliance and pressured Jogaila to accept the faith. At home, Jogaila's nobles also pressured him to convert. Nobles who had converted to Orthodox Christianity, the form of the religion practiced in Russia, advised Jogaila to convert to Orthodoxy and seek an alliance with Russia. Other nobles advised Jogaila to convert to Catholicism, the form of Christianity practiced in western Europe and in Poland.

*This statue of Jogaila (Jagiello) stands in New York City's Central Park.*

In 1386 the issue of religion was settled when the 33-year-old Jogaila was baptized and married Jadwiga, the 12-year-old crown princess of Poland. As a result of the marriage, Grand Duke Jogaila of Lithuania also became king of Poland. As part of the marriage terms, Jogaila ordered his pagan subjects to convert to Catholicism in 1387.

By 1413 all of pagan Lithuania had converted.

The marriage of Jogaila and Jadwiga was a major event in Lithuanian history. Lithuania and Poland, although still independent states, were now allied for a common cause. Together they presented a united front against the German Teutonic Knights and a rival to Muscovy, the growing center of power in Russia. Under the leadership of Lithuania-Poland, the threat from the Teutonic Knights was finally eliminated. In 1410 the combined armies of Lithuania and Poland defeated the Teutonic Knights at the Battle of Tannenberg (or Grünwald). In this famous battle the power of the knights was finally broken. Their lands, the Duchy of Prussia, came under Polish control, and their center of power was confined to the town of Königsberg, present-day Kaliningrad, in Russia.

## When Lithuania Ruled the World

Lithuanian power reached its peak after Jogaila delegated the position of grand duke to his cousin, Vytautas. Known as "the Great" in Lithuanian history, Vytautas was deserving of the name. During his 29-year reign (1401–1430), Vytautas ruled Lithuania independently and joined forces with Jogaila of Poland to defeat the Teutonic Knights once and for all. As Grand Duke of Lithuania, Vytautas ruled over a state that stretched from the Baltic

*A medieval knight on horseback, a symbol of past greatness, is on the coat of arms of Lithuania.*

Sea almost to the Black Sea. Lithuania was one of the largest kingdoms in Europe. On the map of Europe, it looked like Lithuania ruled the known world.

Under Vytautas's enlightened command, Lithuanian princes allowed the people in their conquered lands to govern themselves and practice their own religions. Traders, merchants, scholars, and others from distant parts of Europe were invited to settle in Vilnius. Vytautas's Tatar bodyguards settled in the town. Jews also established settlements in Vilnius, which became famous as a center of Jewish learning. At the royal court, Lithuanian nobles adopted Polish culture and the Slavonic language.

In 1447, Lithuania and Poland became permanently allied under Casimir IV, Jogaila's son. From 1501 the countries had one ruler. In 1569, Lithuania and Poland agreed in the Treaty of Lublin to have one lawmaking body and a king who was elected by the nobles. Lithuania's fate was now linked with that of Poland. Whatever happened to Poland would affect Lithuania, too.

## Sweden and Russia in the Baltic

During the mid-1500s, Lithuania's northern neighbors Latvia and Estonia were being eyed by Russia and Sweden. The Russian czar Ivan the Terrible wanted access to the ice-free Baltic Sea, and to get it he invaded the area in 1558. During the 25-year-long Livonian War, Ivan burned, occupied, and made life miserable for every town in mainland Estonia and the eastern half of Latvia. Nearly two thirds of the population of Estonia perished during the Livonian War and subsequent wars to the year 1629. The German Livonian Knights who had controlled Estonia and Latvia were no match for Ivan's armies or other armies from Poland-Lithuania, Denmark, and Sweden, which also occupied Estonia and Latvia in the hope of acquiring land.

By 1592, Sweden and Poland-Lithuania alone remained to fight each other for Baltic lands. Sweden took control of Riga and most of eastern Latvia and southern

*Peter the Great, during the Great Northern War*

Estonia by 1629. The Swedish kings were interested in improving the lives of the people and tried to end serfdom in Estonia and Latvia. They also introduced elementary schools and a university at Tartu, Estonia. Sweden's rule over Baltic lands was brief, however. Under the rule of its dynamic czar Peter the Great, Russia finally gained its "window on the west." Russian armies ousted Sweden from the Baltic in the early 1700s during the Great

Northern War. The war was terrible in its destructiveness. At the end of the fighting, in 1721, one Russian general was supposed to have said that neither the bark of a dog nor the crowing of a rooster could be heard anywhere from Narva to Riga. But Russia had gained the ice-free ports on the Baltic it had wanted as well as access to the trade goods and ideas of western Europe.

## Lithuania-Poland Disappears

Lithuania-Poland's power as a state came to an end in the 1700s as its neighbors rose to power in its place. Prussia, which had been under Polish control since the early 1400s, began to regain its position as an important state in the early 1600s. Prussia united with the powerful northern German state of Brandenburg in 1618 and by the early 1700s had become a major European military power. Lithuania-Poland, by contrast, was weak. It had no industry and very little agriculture. Unlike Estonia and Latvia, it had no major ports or trade networks with the west. Its ambitious neighbors, Russia, Austria, and Prussia stepped in and began to take it apart, section by section. Three partitions of Lithuania-Poland took place in 1772, 1793, and 1795–1796. Most of Lithuania-Poland became part of Russia, while a small piece of western Lithuania-Poland went to Prussia. Lithuanians became subjects of Russia or

*The interior of a Russian Orthodox Church in Latvia*

Prussia, and their once huge state disappeared from the map of Europe.

## The Baltic Under Russian Rule

Lithuania was totally absorbed into Russia and Prussia, and Estonia and Latvia were now treated as provinces of the Russian empire. Russian laws became the laws of the Baltic lands. The Baltic peoples were forced to learn the Russian language in school. Catholics were persecuted for practicing their religion. All books and

*This drawing shows the forced emigration of Lithuanian peasants in the 1800s.*

newspapers had to be published using the Russian Cyrillic alphabet. Some aspects of life remained unchanged, however. In Estonia and Latvia the German nobles who had been in control of the land since medieval times were allowed to continue ruling at the local level. Baltic Germans joined the Russian imperial army and took jobs in the imperial government.

Peasants suffered the most under Russian rule. Estonian and Latvian peasants had been protected during Sweden's brief rule. Under the Russians their lives were subject to the harshest Russian laws. As serfs they were tied to the land and could not move from it. Escape was punished with brandings and whippings. Estonian and Latvian serfs were finally freed in the early 1800s but had no land to farm and support themselves with. As a result, peasants in the Baltic rose up against the Russians. In 1830, Lithuanians joined Poles in their revolt against Russia. Serfs in Lithuania (and Russia), however, were not freed until 1861. The bleak situation of peasants in the Baltic led to large-scale emigration. In the 1800s, tens of thousands of Lithuanians, and a smaller number of Latvians and Estonians, migrated to the Americas.

By the mid-1800s, Baltic peasants were finally allowed to own land and move about freely. This development made it possible for people to learn new professions and seek jobs in towns and cities. As peasants moved from farms to towns, the cities of the Baltic grew. By 1914, Riga was an important port and city, with more than half a million people. More young people began to attend schools and universities. Writers, poets, and artists began to explore their national past. In the late 1800s and early 1900s, the people of Estonia, Latvia, and Lithuania began to rediscover their native languages, culture, and history. Books and newspapers began to appear in Estonian, Latvian, and Lithuanian. Plays and song festivals became popular. By 1900 almost all Estonians and Latvians could read and write.

# THE HARD ROAD TO FREEDOM

The early 1900s marked a turning point in the history of the Baltic. In 1905, Russia experienced its first revolution. Baltic nationalists took advantage of the democratic changes in Russia to demand self-rule. When the Russian czar was overthrown in the Bolshevik revolution of 1917, calls for Baltic independence grew louder. World War I was still going on, however, and much of the fighting was in and around the Baltic. As Russian armies retreated, German troops occupied the region. Russia's new Communist government was anxious to get out of the war and in 1918 gave the Baltic region to Germany in the Treaty of Brest-Litovsk. With this shift, political leaders in Estonia, Latvia, and Lithuania set up independent governments.

When the Soviet Union tried to regain control of the Baltic in the years following World War I, the Soviet army was turned back by local militias together with foreign assistance from Britain and Scandinavia. In Latvia, German troops stayed behind after the war in the hope of bringing Latvia under German control. The Latvian countryside became a bloody zone where Germans, Bolsheviks, and nationalists fought each other. In Lithuania, Russians

*Latvian independence was declared
in Riga's National Theatre in 1918.*

and Poles fought for control of the city of Vilnius. Finally, in 1920, the Soviet Union signed peace treaties with Estonia, Latvia, and Lithuania and recognized their independence. A new era had begun.

## First Independence: 1920–1939

Major changes took place in the Baltic as a result of independence. Up to 1920, more than half the land had belonged to a few noble families. After 1920, the large estates were broken up and given to peasants as small farms.

Agriculture recovered from the devastation of the war, and the standard of living improved despite the worldwide economic depression of the 1930s. The Baltic countries became exporters of grain and milk. Educational levels also improved as more young people attended schools. Social, cultural, and political organizations flourished in the Baltics during this time, and the national languages developed. Despite the political and economic upheavals of the post-World War I years, the 1920s and 1930s in the Baltic countries were a time of prosperity and hope in the future. In the difficult years to come, the people would look back on this brief time of nationhood with fondness.

## A Brutal War

In 1939, just before the outbreak of World War II, Nazi Germany and the Soviet Union secretly agreed to divide eastern Europe into German and Soviet zones of influence. Estonia and Latvia were placed under Soviet control and Lithuania under German control. In September 1939, Nazi armies marched into Poland, an event that triggered the beginning of World War II. Because Lithuania refused to take part in the Nazi invasion of Poland, it was placed under Soviet rule. The Soviets forced the Baltic countries to allow Russian troops onto their lands, and by 1940, Russian soldiers occupied Estonia, Latvia, and Lithuania.

Elections were held in each country, and members of the Communist Party—the only political party allowed to run—"won" offices. Estonia, Latvia, and Lithuania were made republics of the Soviet Union to the horror of the Baltic peoples. Their brief period of freedom—from 1920 to 1939—had come to an end.

Once in control of the Baltic, the Soviets placed Communists in charge of all aspects of government and the economy. Councils called *soviets* were established at the district, town, and city levels and ran the day-to-day affairs of the countries. Industries once owned and run by Estonians, Latvians, and Lithuanians were placed under Soviet state ownership. Political leaders and outspoken citizens of the once-independent countries were either shot or sent to Siberia, where they died in prison camps. The loss of human life and population as a result of the seizure of the Baltic countries by the Soviet Union was staggering. Within a year of the Soviet takeover, about 1,000 Estonians were arrested and disappeared. Over 10,000 were sent to Siberia in mass deportations that began in June 1941. Many others fled abroad. Lithuania lost 45,000 people and Latvia about 35,000.

Upheaval continued in the Baltic as the prewar agreement between Nazi Germany and the Soviet Union proved to be short-lived. In 1941 the Nazi leader Adolf Hitler turned against his one-time Soviet ally Joseph Stalin and

*Latvian peasants "vote" in an election of the Supreme Soviet of the USSR in 1941. The Soviet flag and a portrait of Joseph Stalin are in the background.*

invaded Russia. The tiny Baltic countries stood in the path of Hitler's well-equipped and disciplined army and felt the full impact of the German invasion. Some people in the Baltic, however, looked upon the Nazis as the lesser of two evil masters. They supported the German occupation and helped the Nazis. Nevertheless, the German occupation caused great disruption within Baltic society. Families divided along political lines as some members supported the Germans and fought the Soviets. Nationalists who wanted to regain the independence of their countries fought both the Nazis and the Soviets. Neighbors regarded each other with suspicion or hatred, and human trust disappeared from everyday life. The people of the Baltic—without armies or allies—were crushed between two opposing totalitarian systems. In the darkest years of World War II, survival became the only goal.

## A Time of Terror

The people of Europe suffered terribly during World War II. Cities were bombed to pieces, and whole populations fled as armies approached. In the Baltic, Estonians, Latvians, and Lithuanians either joined the German army to fight the Russians or were drafted against their will. Others in the Baltic were forced to work for the Nazis as slave laborers in factories and on farms. Many others left their homes, businesses, and careers and escaped to the West. Partisans, those who worked against the Nazis, were hanged or shot if captured. Many in the region fled the Nazi terror and took refuge in the forests, hoping to avoid the destruction.

Jews in Estonia, Latvia, and Lithuania were a special target of the Nazis. All over the Baltic, as elsewhere in Nazi-occupied Europe, Jews were rounded up and taken away to concentration camps. In Vilnius, Jews were herded into ghettoes, where they were isolated from the rest of the population. Jewish defenders bravely resisted the destruction of the Vilnius ghetto, but in the end, Nazi forces won out. Men, women, and children were collected and taken out of the city in trucks. Many were shot and buried in the forests. Others were sent to concentration camps, where they were worked and starved to death or were killed outright in gas chambers. Almost the entire Jewish population of Lithuania—one of the largest in eastern Europe—perished during World War II. Latvian Jews were also wiped out. Estonia lost nearly 200,000 people during the war, Latvia 450,000, and Lithuania 475,000. The Baltic region became one vast graveyard.

## Sweet Freedom Is Lost

By the end of 1944, Soviet troops had reconquered the Baltic, forcing the Germans out. In fierce fighting the cities and towns of Estonia, Latvia, and Lithuania were flattened by attacks from the ground and the air as the retreating German soldiers fought off the Russian advance. Crops in the fields were burned by armies from both sides. Germans who had been living in the Baltic were sent to Siberia or were deported to Germany. Those Estonians, Latvians, and Lithuanians who had worked with the Nazis against the Soviets were executed or sent to Siberia. Writers, teachers, scientists, and scholars—the nations' intellectuals—fled across the Baltic Sea to Sweden ahead of the Soviets. Some escaped to freedom in Western Europe and joined a massive refugee population. Those who were captured were sent to Siberia as punishment. Many died there, never to see their homelands again. For those who survived the war and remained behind, there was only grief and horror. Sweet freedom had been lost.

In the years 1944–1955, the Soviets reestablished Communist control in the Baltic with an iron fist. Symbols of Estonian, Latvian, and Lithuanian history were done away with. The people were not allowed to sing their national anthems or display their national flags. If they did, they were severely punished. Monuments to Baltic heroes were destroyed. Books about the past were outlawed or rewritten from the Soviet point of view. Private property was forbidden. Privately owned farms were seized by the state and turned into collectives. Peasants became workers on these huge farms and turned over the crops they raised to the state. Factories that had survived the bombings of the war were also seized from their private owners and placed under state control. The Baltic currencies were replaced by the Russian ruble. Those who had banked their money in the old currencies lost their savings.

During this time, people who resisted the Soviet takeover were executed or deported. Some fled the Soviet terror and hid in the region's many forests. The Baltic "forest brothers" fought Soviet soldiers from their woodland hiding places. The Soviets were too strong for the forest brothers, however, and the Baltic resistance movement was crushed by the early 1950s.

## Russian Transplants

The peoples of the Baltic despised Soviet rule and resisted it as best they could. But they were totally powerless against one tactic. After the war the Soviet leader Joseph Stalin ordered large numbers of Russians moved into the Baltic to work and live. They came from western Russia, Belarus, and Ukraine. This policy of moving Russians into the Baltic came to be known as Russification. Their numbers already reduced by war, deportation, and execution, Estonians, Latvians, and Lithuanians feared they would become minorities in their own countries. They had good reason to be fearful. Russians in the Baltics were given the homes and apartments of natives of the Baltic region. Estonians, Latvians, and Lithuanians had to wait on housing lists for an apartment to become available. Often the wait extended for years. Russians were also favored on the job. They received the best assignments, while native Estonians, Latvians, or Lithuanians were passed over.

*In Tallinn, a street sign in Russian appears
above a hand carved wooden sign in Estonian.*

The years of Soviet rule were a depressing time for everyone in the Baltic. Young people growing up in the Baltic countries heard about their country's period of independence from their parents or grandparents but saw only Russian domination in their everyday lives. Police spies kept track of what people said and did and punished those who spoke out or had a different opinion. There was no freedom of speech or action. Everywhere they turned, the native Baltic peoples were made to feel like strangers in their own land. To survive, people pretended to believe Soviet teachings and avoided political discussions.

In addition, the Soviets distrusted outsiders and made

sure that contacts between the Baltic countries and the West were limited. Tourist travel within the Baltic region was limited by Soviet authorities. The practice of religion was also discouraged. Churches were closed, and priests were sent away. Religious paintings and statues were destroyed in an effort to wipe out all influences that might challenge communism. Like the rest of Soviet-dominated Eastern Europe, the Baltic countries were hidden from the rest of the world by an "iron curtain." Outsiders knew little about the peoples of the Baltic and their way of life. Most of the countries of the world quietly accepted Soviet rule of the Baltic countries. The United States, however, never recognized the incorporation of the Baltic countries into the Soviet Union.

## Disastrous Industrialization

After World War II the Soviets turned Estonia and Latvia into centers of polluting, toxic industry. Without consulting the peoples of the Baltic, Soviet managers hundreds of miles away in Moscow planned and ran the economies of the region, often with harmful results. Oil shale strip mines were started in Estonia, for instance, and the shale was burned to make electricity. Instead of disposing of the slag heaps and the ash from the burned-off shale, the Soviets allowed it to build up in black mountains of toxic waste or in huge fields. The pollutants from the waste seeped into the ground, making the soil useless for farming. In Ignalina, Lithuania, the Soviets built a nuclear reactor with no regard to faults in its design. The health risks to the Baltic population were never considered.

The Soviets also had new factories built in Riga, Tallinn, and other Baltic cities. These factories churned out metal products, chemicals, heavy machinery, timber, pulp, paper, processed foods, electrical appliances, and many other consumer items. Most of these manufactured products were sold in the Soviet Union or shipped from Baltic ports to the Soviet Union's trading partners overseas.

While turning the mainly rural and agricultural Baltic countries into urban, industrialized republics of the Soviet Union, the Soviets neglected and damaged the environment everywhere. Because of poor planning, factories and power plants were built in the middle of farmland. Bad management allowed industrial waste from factories, chemical plants, and paper mills to spew into the air and run into streams, rivers, and lakes. The air and waterways of the Baltic became severely polluted. Toxic substances such as sulfur dioxide fouled the air not only in the Baltic countries but also in neighboring countries, such as Finland. Water became contaminated and was unfit for drinking. The once-plentiful supply of freshwater and salt-water fish died off as a result of chemical spills. Untreated sewage from houses and apartments was allowed to run off into sources of drinking water. Life-expectancy rates fell as people came down with diseases caused by pollution. Today the people of the Baltic still live with the terrible effects of Soviet industrialization.

## Rebirth

The years of Soviet rule were like a night without an end for the peoples of the Baltic. Deprived of their freedom, history, and land, Estonians, Latvians, and Lithuanians became prisoners in their own countries. Above all, they feared they would become invisible as more and more Russians and other Soviet peoples were moved into the Baltic. The voices of the people were never completely silenced, however, and the young in particular often exploded in rage against Soviet controls.

In 1972, Romas Kalanta, a Lithuanian student in Kaunas, set himself on fire in protest against Soviet control of his country. Soon after his death, thousands of young Lithuanians rioted. Many were arrested, but opposition continued. In 1980, students and workers in Estonia protested and went on strike. A 1980 rock concert in Tallinn created even more trouble for the Soviets. Music fans rioted when the concert was called off halfway through the performance. As fans rampaged through the

streets of Tallinn, they yelled out slogans critical of the
Soviet authorities. Soccer matches and basketball games
between Baltic teams and the Russian team presented
opportunities for the Baltic players and fans to sing anti-
Soviet songs. Protests were also carried out by Baltic
teachers, writers, and environmentalists. They risked their
lives and careers by speaking out against the forced use of
the Russian language, the suppression of Baltic culture,
and the destruction of the environment. Many of the
protestors were sent to prison because of their actions.
Some were never seen again.

In the mid-1980s, events in Moscow, the Soviet capital,
brought about dramatic changes within the Soviet Union.
As part of an attempt to cure the Soviet Union's economic
ills and other failings, the new Soviet leader Mikhail
Gorbachev encouraged a policy of openness, or *glasnost*, in
Soviet government and society. No longer would criticism
of the government be met with arrest or harassment. The
loosening of restrictions on free speech gave rise to even
greater outspokenness in the Baltic countries.

The outspokenness took many forms. In Estonia,
protestors demanded the end of phosphate mining, a serious
hazard to the already-damaged environment. Gorbachev
gave in to the Estonians' demands, and the mining was
brought to a halt. Similar demands were made in Latvia and
Lithuania. As in Estonia, the Soviets decided to back down.

Folk festivals, long a symbol of Baltic national identity, became opportunities for dissent. In 1987 the old national flags of the Baltic countries were displayed at an Estonian song festival. It was the first time since World War II that the flags had been seen in public. No one was arrested. Also in 1987 an event in Latvia captured the imagination of Baltic peoples and attracted the attention of the West. On June 14, Latvian dissidents gathered at the Freedom Monument in Riga to remember the Latvians deported by the Soviets in 1941. Soon after the first meeting at the monument, many other Latvians came to leave flowers on the site. There were demonstrations in several Latvian cities, and soon the other Baltic countries joined in. It seemed that Gorbachev's policies were actually helping to unravel Soviet rule in the republics.

When the Soviet Union officially acknowledged the secret agreement between Hitler and Stalin that had placed the Baltic under Soviet control, the peoples of the Baltic could scarcely believe the news. A part of history that had been hidden and denied by the Soviet Union for 50 years was now out in the open! Finally they could speak freely about the deportations and executions carried out by the Soviets. With the truth out in the open, there was no telling what would happen next. Many in the Baltic believed that freedom might actually be achieved. At first it seemed like a wild, reckless thought, but enough

people in the Baltic countries believed it could happen. With belief came reality.

## No Turning Back

With these developments new political groups began to form in the Baltic during the late 1980s. At first they asked for greater self-rule within the Soviet system, but their actual goal was complete independence from the Soviet Union. On August 23, 1989, two million people linked hands between the cities of Tallinn, Estonia, and Vilnius, Lithuania, in a giant human chain. Their purpose was to recall the 1939 pact between Nazi Germany and the Soviet Union. The linking of hands became a dramatic symbol of the Baltic's desire for freedom. Every day seemed to bring new and exciting changes.

The Soviet Union agreed to give the Baltic countries more control over their economies, but that was not enough to satisfy the independent-minded Baltic leaders. In early 1990, Sajūdis, a group devoted to Lithuania's independence, won a majority of seats in Lithuania's parliament and in March of the same year boldly declared Lithuania independent. Similar independence movements were organized in Latvia and Estonia, where new political leaders were elected.

The Soviets did not allow the Baltics to slip away quietly, however. In 1991, Soviet troops and police seized

*As a symbol of their desire for freedom, two million people of the Baltics linked hands to form a human chain in 1989.*

*Lithuanians demonstrate for independence in early 1990.*

buildings in Vilnius and Riga. People died in the violence that erupted, and it seemed as if the Soviets would crack down on the independence movements. But the crackdown never came. In August 1991, opponents of *glasnost* tried to force Gorbachev from power. The Baltic independence leaders used the period of chaos and confusion in the

*Books by Sid Fleischman*

# JINGO DJANGO

# JINGO DJANGO

## by Sid Fleischman

*Illustrated by Eric von Schmidt*

*An Atlantic Monthly Press Book*
Little, Brown and Company
BOSTON     TORONTO

LIBRARY OF CONGRESS CATALOG CARD NO. 75–140481

T 05/71

FIRST EDITION

ATLANTIC–LITTLE, BROWN BOOKS
ARE PUBLISHED BY
LITTLE, BROWN AND COMPANY
IN ASSOCIATION WITH
THE ATLANTIC MONTHLY PRESS

*Published simultaneously in Canada*
*by Little, Brown & Company (Canada) Limited*

PRINTED IN THE UNITED STATES OF AMERICA

*For Marty and Carol and Henry*

# Contents

# JINGO DJANGO

# 1

## GENERAL DIRTY-FACE JIM SCURLOCK

I'd just as soon disremember Mrs. Daggatt and General Dirty-Face Jim Scurlock. But I'm not likely to forget them either.

Mrs. Daggatt was big as a skinned ox. When I awoke she was lumbering through the boys' dormitory. It was still dark and she was holding a three-pronged candle holder like it was the Devil's own pitchfork. In the flaring yellow light she looked us over as if she were picking a lamb for slaughter. Her eyes settled on me.

"Rise up and follow," she said.

I took all the time I could pulling on my linsey-woolsey shirt, making a mux of the sleeves and keeping her standing. I think I was the only boy in the orphan house who wasn't mortally afraid of her — at least, I wouldn't show it.

"Lively, now."

"I can't find my shoes," I said. The truth was I had traded them off for a breakfast of oysters and biscuits the last time I had run away. The year was 1854 and it was mud time — early April. Shoes were a pesky bother in mud time.

She shot me an impatient scowl. "Bare feet'll do. Come along! There's a gentleman waiting."

I knew what that meant. She was hiring me out. If there was a mean, no-souled job offered, Mrs. Daggatt was always glad to apprentice one of her strays. Not that we ever saw a penny for our labors. Every copper found its way directly into Mrs. Daggatt's fat, pink hand and disappeared forever.

Well, I could be the most contrary apprentice in Boston. I didn't mean to stay hired out for long.

I followed her along the hall and down the old stairs. The floorboards creaked and groaned under her great weight.

"Maybe my pa's come to fetch me," I said.

"He's never coming to fetch you," she snapped.

That suited me fine, though I never let on to anyone. It was my closest secret. I might as well confess the truth — I'm a liar. I was always making up howling good stories about my pa. I'd say he stood seven feet tall and was master of the fastest China clipper in the trade. Oh, he was shipwrecked many a time, I'd say, and captured by Chinese pirates once and almost eaten by cannibals twice. And it wouldn't surprise me if he was shipwrecked again, but one day he'd turn up and snatch me out of Mrs. Daggatt's confounded Beneficent Orphan House and off we'd frolic to sea again.

The truth was that my pa might have been a fishmonger

4

for all I knew, or a common thief. A murderer, even. I could barely recollect him, except that he was a one-legged man with teeth as black as tar. He'd shed himself of me when I was five or six, after my ma died, and if I never laid eyes on him again I'd reckon myself lucky.

I never talked to anyone about my ma. I remembered her dark hair blowing about on a windy day, and the flash of her gold earrings and even the sound of her laughter. That was all I remembered, but it was something to hold on to and I held it close.

"Now mind what I say," Mrs. Daggatt grumbled. "You'll answer the gentleman's questions with 'Yes, sir.' Stand erect, hands at your sides, and show proper respect. Now whack your cheeks to put some color into them."

I gave my cheeks a pat or two and we hauled up at Mrs. Daggatt's back parlor. The grandfather clock was striking as we entered and I shot a glance at the gentleman standing with his back to the window.

I knew him at once. I'd seen him on the streets many a time, blowing his army trumpet and followed by his raggedy pack of soot devils. It was the chimney master — General Dirty-Face Jim Scurlock.

He was a flop-eared man with a dented top hat and a nose as heavy as a turnip. His twitchy eyes settled on me like a found penny, and his face broke into a huge smile.

"Aye, there's the lad I be lookin' for," he laughed. "No bigger'n a pint o' cider — that's the ticket, me dear Daggatt. But he is a bit all skin and bones, ain't he?"

"There's small choice in rotten apples," Mrs. Daggatt

5

grunted. "But his cheeks are healthy — you can see that. His name is Jingo. Jingo Hawks."

"Aye, there's a bloom to his cheeks," the chimney master agreed, moving closer. He felt the muscles in my arm and then pried open my jaws. He checked my teeth as if he were buying a horse. Finally he stepped back with a grin and blew his nose in a large blue handkerchief.

"Be ye a climbing boy, Jingo?" he asked.

"Yes, sir," I said.

"Fine. First rate. Not afraid of high places and dark places, eh? There's a brave lad. Do ye know your age?"

"Yes, sir," I said, although it was a mystery to me when I was born or where I was born. I made up dates and places to suit my fancy.

"He's eleven or twelve or thirteen by my reckoning," Mrs. Daggatt put in.

"A bit oldish," the chimney master said, and gave my dark eyes and curly black hair a squint and a grin. "Brown as a berry, ain't he? What brand of boy do ye take him for, me dear Daggatt?"

"Mohawk Indian for all I know. He's learned his letters behind my back and can sign his own name. I hope you won't hold that against him, General."

"I'll overlook it," the chimney master grinned, and then rolled his eyes in mock horror. "Be ye an Indian, lad! Can I count on ye not to lift my scalp, Jingo?"

I didn't favor him with an answer and he roared out laughing. I stood like a statue and watched the clock pendulum dawdling back and forth, slicing seconds off the hour. If I had savage blood it would please me hugely, but I knew better than to take Mrs. Daggatt's word for it. Still, my head rattled with the oddments of a language no one at the orphan house had ever heard before. I could cough up words like *mishto* and *sar shan* and *hatchi-witchu,* but I no longer clearly recollected what they meant.

The chimney master gave me his twitchy eye. "Ain't ye a lucky lad, eh? I'll learn you a splendid profession. Aye, a noble profession."

"Yes, sir."

"How'd ye like to be one of General Jim Scurlock's famous chimney squirrels, eh? Does it take your fancy?"

"Yes, sir," I said. And *no, sir,* I said to myself. His nose would turn bluer'n a whetstone before he turned me into a chimney sweep. But I was answering him according to Mrs. Daggatt's own exact instructions.

"Now ye ain't one of them nippers given to running away, be you?"

"Yes, sir."

He didn't seem to be listening. "And you're an honest lad. I can see that, Jingo. Ye wouldn't cadge and steal and filch from your true friend and benefactor."

"Yes, sir," I answered.

That caught him up short. "What's that, lad? Did I hear ye right?"

"Yes, sir."

Mrs. Daggatt shot me a glance like the milltail o' thunder, but the chimney master was already looking at me down one side of his nose. "Don't try to flummox me. Can't you answer anything but *yes, sir* and *yes, sir* and another *yes, sir?*"

"Yes, sir."

His mouth puckered and then he bent closer so that we were almost nose to nose. "Ever seen the sun shine at night?"

"Yes, sir."

"Ever heard a cat bark like a dog?"

"Yes, sir."

"Be ye dull-witted, boy?"

"Yes, sir."

I thought he'd chuck me for sure. But he broke into a devilish smile. He gave his coattails a flick and turned to Mrs. Daggatt. "He's buffle-brained, for certain. First rate. First rate and a half. It don't require a scholar to sweep chimneys. I'll take him, me dear Daggatt!"

# 2

## THE SOOT DEVIL

Fire and furies! I had outfoxed myself. The worst of it was the look Mrs. Daggatt shot at me. It was a smile. It was a smirk. It was sour enough to make a pig squeal.

"Come along, lad," General Scurlock beamed. "And there'll be a ten-dollar gold piece if ye find a thing I be looking for. A chimney-hid thing. How does that strike ye, eh?"

I could see sunrise glowing up through the window. I'd make a flying, bald-headed dash for it as soon as we hit the street. He wasn't going to sniggle me with chimney-hid things. He wasn't going to dangle a gold piece in front of my nose to keep me from running off.

But that man could read thoughts. The moment Mrs. Daggatt shut the door behind us he snatched me by the left ear and hoisted me up to my toes.

"I'll twist your ear off before ye give me the slip," he grinned, his twitchy eye a-flutter. "That's the first lesson I learn me soot devils, Jingo. And I'll snap your *other* ear off if ye get so much as a faraway look in your eye. That's your second lesson! And if ye do slope away I'll find ye quick and certain. I've never lost a climbing boy yet. That's your *third* lesson."

I thought he'd never turn loose of my ear. "But sir," I said before he laid down more lessons than I could bear. "But sir, you rescued me from the orphan house. I'm eternally grateful. I'm eager to learn a splendid, noble profession in the chimneys." And then I added for good luck, "Do you think I might grow up to be a sweep master like yourself?"

"Buffle-brained," he wheezed, easing off on my ear at last. "Let's march."

Beneath all his chuckles and smiles he was a scaresome man, and I elected to keep ears on my head until after breakfast. I'd dodge him in my own good time. A full stomach was the *first* lesson in running away and I'd almost forgot it.

Before long we hauled up at his shack along the river. His other boys were waiting under a large shed that was a kind of ash dump. He sold those ashes for fertilizer or for making soap.

We stood looking at each other. They were a silent, beaten lot. I felt sorry for them and I reckon they felt sorry for me. They were bundled up in blackened rags and wore oilskin chimney hats pointed like dunce caps.

"Sampson," he said to a skinny, red-haired boy, "fetch Jingo a scraper." Then he turned to an even skinnier boy with soot-rimmed eyes. "Casharagoo, fetch him a brush and a hat."

"I'm dreadful hungry," I said.

11

"Aye, a fine bit of cling-john and coffee'll be waiting when your work's done, lad," he answered, and ducked into his shack.

There was no getting the best of that man. Breakfast was just a tricksy promise! But he hadn't got the best of me yet, either.

He reappeared all dandied up for the streets. "Fall in!" he shouted and led his company of soot devils across the yard. Each of us was burdened with large hemp blankets.

You never saw such a shivering, hungry and ragged procession. General Scurlock wasn't exactly spic and span himself, but he was warm enough in his general's faded blue frock coat. A cavalry sword dangled from a red sash

tied around his middle, like bunting, and you'd think he was marching off to war.

The cobbled streets were still morning wet and the windows seemed lacquered over with sunlight. From time to time General Scurlock would lift an old trumpet to his lips and blast loud enough to wake snakes. Then he'd let go with his street cry.

> Sweep *ho!* Sweep *ho!*
> Here come General Scurlock's soot devils!
> Sweep for your soot, *ho!*
> From the bottom to the top,
> Without a ladder or a rope!
> Sweep *ho!* Sweep *ho-o-o-o!*

13

I'd heard it many a time from the orphan house. I had done harder work than scraping down a chimney, but I felt six kinds of a fool marching along in that dunce cap. I dropped it behind the first bush we came to.

But Casharagoo fished it up with his scraper and snuck it back to me. "Old Split-Foot'll give you a whippin'," he whispered.

"I've been whipped before," I said.

"You'll need it in the flues," he muttered. "It'll keep the muck out of your hair."

He gazed at me through his wispy, soot-rimmed eyes and I nodded. "What kind of flapdoodle general is he?" I asked.

"That off-ox? Weren't no general at all. Just puts on the flamigigs. He was in the Mexico war a few years back. Lucky if he rose to the rank of private."

I canted the dunce cap back on my head and General Scurlock gave another blast of his lungs.

Sweep *ho!* Sweep *ho!*

Here and there along the streets a window would rise or a door would open and there'd be a beckoning gesture. He'd peel off a couple of boys to clean the chimneys.

"And don't forget to fetch me back the ashes," he warned.

Finally there was no one left in his ragged army but me. We ended up in an old sidehill house on Salem Street. It had a short chimney at the kitchen and a long one shooting up through an overhanging second story.

14

The back roof almost sloped down to the ground, and that put ideas in my head.

General Scurlock stuck his head up the parlor chimney and said it was a wonder the soot hadn't caught fire, it was so caked up. He haggled with the old widow who owned the place and she finally agreed to thirty-eight cents for the first story and twenty cents for the second. "Nothing extra for clearing out the swallows' nests, me good lady," he added generously.

General Scurlock fixed my hemp blanket across the fireplace to keep the soot and ash out of the parlor. Then he motioned me behind the blanket.

"Up ye go, Jingo."

I took one look up the long, narrow flue and said, "No, sir." The bit of sunlight at the top seemed a mile high.

"Ye ain't scared?" he chuckled.

"Yes, sir," I said.

"Why, that's a good, snug flue. Just your size. The first time's the hardest, lad. I'll give ye a lift up."

"No, sir."

"Ain't ye forgetting that chimney-hid thing? It might be waiting for ye up there." He plucked a ten-dollar gold piece from his pocket and flashed it before my eyes. "And I'll be waiting for ye down here with this, Jingo Hawks. Think of that!"

"I aim to stay right here on the ground," I said.

With that he grabbed hold and gave me a heave up the chimney. "Squirrel up there! Once ye reach the top scrape your way back down."

I managed to brace myself against the bricks, and then with a foothold in the old mortar joints raised myself out of his reach.

"I calculate this is as high as I'm going," I said. Now that I was in the flue I broke into a sweat at the thought of climbing to the sky.

But he drew his sword and gave me a sharp prod. I scurried up and out of reach, again.

"Use your back and elbows, lad. Keep a-going. And if ye turn up a whale's tooth — why that's the chimney-hid thing. Up toward the top, most likely, and sooted over. Spy out the broken bricks and every deepish crack, eh?"

"I'm as far as I aim to climb," I answered, wedging myself in as best I could.

He couldn't reach me with his sword point and he was too large himself to squirrel up the flue after me. But he was a chuckling man and a tricksy man and before long he had built a straw fire under me. The smoke and the rising heat began to do me in.

I took one fearsome look at the sky and clawed my way toward it. I scuffed my toes and elbows raw, and all the while he stood below chuckling. That infernal *hatchi-witchu!* I thought.

When I reached daylight I wiped my eyes clear of soot and gazed out, past the rooftops, toward the harbor. I could pick out the orphan house and supposed Mrs. Daggatt was already counting the pennies old Split-Foot would pay her for my labors.

Well, she could wait till the crack of doom. I wasn't

going back down that chimney, but I began scraping away. I calculated General Scurlock would duck out of the fireplace when chunks of soot began to fall. A moment later I started down the sloping back roof on my sweaty hands and feet. I tried not to make a sound. When I ran out of roof I wasn't more than ten feet off the ground. I jumped into a row of tall bushes and slipped away.

I don't know how long General Dirty-Face Jim Scurlock stood behind the fireplace blanket waiting for me to come down.

# 3

# THE CHIMNEY-HID THING

That afternoon I spied a one-legged man at India Wharf.
I froze on the spot as if a black cat might cross my path.
I didn't reckon he was my pa, but he might have been,
and the thought put me in a thumping sweat.

I spun back around the corner of a ship chandler's shop and almost charged into Casharagoo.

"Jingo," he said with a lightning flash of teeth. I hadn't seen him smile before. "Old Split-Foot's coughin' fire and brimstone. You're doin' cleverly, all in all. But he reasoned you'd turn up along the waterside."

Sea gulls were squalling overhead. "I aim to sign aboard a clipper ship and sail to China," I said.

Casharagoo glanced back over his shoulder. "Take my best advice and make a straight shirttail out of here. I've been caught on the wharfs more'n once. Don't you know he's put a dollar reward on you? And he ain't far behind, over at Long Wharf passin' out the news. We're all out lookin' for you."

That dollar reward must have been a torment to Casharagoo. He as much as had it clasped in his hand. But his eyes kept darting about and he seemed eager for me to be gone. "Cut dirt before it's too late," he said.

But I stood there like a stump. "I've changed my mind, Casharagoo. I ain't had a bite to eat and my stomach's hollow as a gourd. I hid the morning in a rain barrel and it was half full of water. I'm wore out hopping about like a flea. I calculate I might as well give myself up."

He gazed at me through his sad, blinking eyes. I figured he could collect that reward and then directly I'd run off again. "Has your brains turned to sawdust?" he said.

"Scraping chimneys is a fine, noble profession. First

19

rate and a half. You just haul me in."

"Tarnation!" he exploded. "Don't you know he'll take your hide off? And soon as you grow up too big for the flues, why he'll kick you out by the seat of your breeches! It's no proper trade at all."

"My mind's made up," I said.

"So's mine. Peel out and keep a sharp eye until you get your senses back."

Suddenly it came to me. If I could make good my runaway he and the other sweeps might be eager to try it again.

"Quick now!"

I nodded. "Quick as I can." We almost shook hands, but didn't. He turned and I lurched away.

I dodged back to the North End where I had tucked the chimney brush and scraper in a woodpile. I'd have traded them both for a biscuit. But it dawned on me that the one place General Dirty-Face Jim Scurlock wouldn't expect to find me was inside a flue.

Directly I began knocking at back doors and offered to do a bit of scraping for something to eat. A gentle-eyed woman took me in. Her name was Mrs. Jenks.

She said her oven would hardly draw. I gazed up the one-story chimney and then shook my head as if I knew what I was about. "It's dreadful caked with soot, m'am," I said. "I'm surprised your chimney ain't caught fire." And then I added, "nothing extra for clearing out the swallows' nests."

I chipped and scraped and brushed in that flue until

the sun went down. When I finished and lit a small fire it drew like an eight-knot breeze. I felt enormously pleased with myself.

She came in from the yard where she was boiling clothes in a wash kettle, stirring them with a ship's oar, and clicked her teeth as she looked me over. I was soot and ashes from head to toe. "You poor, dear orphan," she sighed.

"I'm not an orphan, m'am," I answered stoutly and tried to prove it. I said my pa had started out in the flues and now he was master of a China clipper and I meant to follow in his own grand footsteps.

It's not likely that she believed me, but she pretended she did, and marched me out to the yard and tried to scrub me down for supper. I told her I could scrub myself. It was candlelight before I finished. She stuffed me with turnips and fish cakes and all the bean porridge I could eat. Before I left she gave me a chunk of brown bread tied up in an old handkerchief, and that was the last I saw of her. She was uncommon nice, and I was sorry I had told her those lies.

The night was dark and I lurked about waiting for it to get darker still. General Scurlock would give me up in a week or so, I thought, and a fresh hiding place took my fancy. If he wouldn't expect to find me in a flue, he'd *never* think to look for me in the orphan house.

The scheme near took my breath away. I'd be walking on cat-ice every moment, but I would chance it and humbug the sweep master and Mrs. Daggatt, both!

I shied about in the trees and watched the lights of the orphan house go out upstairs and down. It seemed an eternity before Mrs. Daggatt retired for the night. The doors would be locked tight, but that wouldn't keep me out.

I climbed an old branchy elm and was on the roof quick as a squirrel. I had three stone chimneys to choose from. One led down to the west parlor, which was only used on occasions, and I decided on it.

I slipped inside and let myself down, scuttling like a crab, elbow by elbow and toe by toe. It was a black, fearful way down, but I tried not to think about it.

At the bottom the fireplace was large enough to roast an ox. It was swept clean of ashes. Mrs. Daggatt was a bear for cleanliness.

But I had to be careful not to leave footprints. I stood on the hearth and peered about the room. Most of the chairs and things were covered with heavy muslin sheets and they had the glowering look of headstones in a graveyard.

I meant to spend a week in that chimney. I would come out mostly at night to forage the kitchen for things to eat. And I meant to make myself as comfortable as possible.

A sea hammock, I thought!

Well, it took me most of the night to rig it up. I used one of the points of the chimney scraper to chip out a deep crevice in the mortar between the great fire bricks, about eight feet up, on one side of the flue and then the other. It was mouse work. I had to be careful not to make a clatter.

When I finished I returned to the hearth, scooped up the mortar chips and poured them into the ugly vase that always stood on the mantelpiece. Then I snatched a sheet off the nearest chair.

I made large knots in two corners and drew the sheet up the flue with me. I snugged one end in the upright crevice and pulled hard and downward against the knot. *Mishto!* It held. Feeling my way like a blind man, I slung the sheet across the flue and worked the other end deep between the bricks. The knot took a firm purchase at the top of the open mortar joint and I gave the sheet another test. *Mishto!* again.

I climbed in gently as a snail. I barely dared breathe for fear the whole thing would give way. But it didn't. Before long I was feeling snug as a seaman. My hammock sagged about three feet above the open fireplace and I considered myself safe from discovery.

I bit off a chunk of brown bread and fancied myself slung in the foc'sle of a China clipper with my pa on deck issuing orders in his soft but gallant voice. Then I forced these moonstruck ramblings out of my head. I was beginning to believe my own vaporish lies.

I slept most of the day. Not a soul came into the west parlor. But the following day, late in the afternoon, I could hear Mrs. Daggatt grumbling and waddling about the room.

And then I saw her hand. I saw it reach up like a fat pink claw and grasp a thing corner-snugged behind the inner ledge of the chimney crosspiece. I held my breath for fear she'd peer up into the flue. But she didn't. And then her hand was gone.

It seemed less than a minute before she put it back. And then *she* was gone and I had the west parlor to myself.

Of course I scuttled down out of my hammock. The thing was soot-blackened and shaped like a powder horn.

I knew what it was at once. Here was General Scurlock's chimney-hid thing!

It was a whale's tooth.

24

# 4

## MR. JEFFREY PEACOCK, GENT.

The late afternoon sun glowed like moonlight through the parlor curtains. I dropped to my feet to have a closer look at this chimney-hid thing.

I polished the soot off on my breeches and saw scrimshaw markings carved and tattooed all over that whale's tooth. It was nothing uncommon. I'd seen heaps of scrimshaw along Indian Wharf. Whaling men were forever carving mottoes and pictures on whales' teeth to pass the time at sea. Some of them took your breath away, with spidery views of ships and spouting whales and far-off places. They weren't worth much, as far as I knew.

But this one was worth a ten-dollar gold piece to General Scurlock, and that sent my mind whirling. I'd wait till dark, around midnight maybe, and toe it to old Split-Foot's ash shed. I'd give it to Casharagoo; he could claim the reward and we'd divvy it down the middle.

But that's as far as I got in my thoughts. I heard footsteps and made a cat-leap back into the flue. It was Mrs. Daggatt.

"Come in, sir," I heard her say in a voice as smooth as

lard. "I don't usually receive callers this late in the day. Especially not without a *proper* appointment, but I can see you're a special fine gentleman." I heard the shrouds whipped off the furniture. "Sit down, sir. I don't usually have a moment off my feet. My flock of orphans hardly leave time to catch my breath. Now then, what was it you said your name was?"

"I didn't, madam," he replied. "I gave you my card."

"Glory be, of course you did. Tush! Here it is in my hand."

Wasn't she putting on airs, though, I thought! And all the while she'd be skinning him with her hawk's eyes. She'd probably already weighed and bit every coin in his purse, and from her manner she must have reckoned it considerable. She read off his card as reverently as if it were a bank note.

"Jeffrey Peacock, Gent. I knew you were a true gentleman right off, sir! And what brings you to our poor orphanage, Mr. Peacock? Is it a little apprentice you'd like to take home with you?"

"In a manner of speaking."

"My little girls can scrub, scour and sew. They're proper trained, I assure you. My boys are strong and healthy. Young dray horses, they are! Is it boy or girl you've come for?"

"A boy, madam."

"I'll choose you a fine chap. Indeed I will."

He paused. "The boy I want would be about twelve years old."

26

"Oh, I've a good supply of twelve-year-olds, Mr. Peacock."

"His name would be Jango."

"*Jingo!* Is that who you mean! Tush, Mr. Peacock. He's not the chap for you. A bad bargain, Jingo is. Slippery as an eel. Why, before your back was half-turned he'd make off with your fine gold-headed walking stick."

"Capital," he answered evenly. "That's to my liking. A thief."

I bristled at hearing myself branded a thief. Slippery, for sure, and a bad bargain, maybe, but Mrs. Daggatt was laying it on almighty thick about the gold-headed walking stick.

She seemed kicked speechless by his reply. And then I wondered if Mr. Peacock wasn't laughing to himself. Maybe he was putting on airs of his own. *Avali!* I thought. Mrs. Daggatt had met her match.

But why me? He'd got my name wrong, but he'd come close and I wondered what mischief he was about. I had certainly never heard of any Jeffrey Peacock, Gent. Maybe he was a highwayman, a knight of the road like Captain Thunderbolt, and I found the thought dreadfully pleasing.

Mrs. Daggatt finally got her wits back. "Bless you," she said piously. "I understand perfectly, Mr. Peacock. Indeed I do. You hope to take my shabbiest castoff and turn the little maggot into a fine Christian gentleman such as yourself. Commendable, sir."

"That's not my intention at all, madam. I would consider it a service if you would fetch the lad."

27

Silence again. Her head must have been given another spin. Then the tone of her voice hardened. "That's quite impossible," she said.

"Indeed, madam?"

"If it's Jingo you're set on he's already spoken for. Apprenticed out."

"To whom?"

"That's a matter of confidence, sir. But it would cost a pretty penny to buy up his contract, I assure you."

"How much?"

She now had a solid grip on the business. I could almost hear her run up figures in her head. The walking stick would start the bidding. If he were wearing a silk cravat it would lift the sum a digit or two. And I pitied him if he had stepped into her parlor with a well-brushed top hat. It would double the price.

"Two hundred dollars," she announced finally.

"Fetch him," Mr. Peacock replied calmly, and I imagined Mrs. Daggatt could have bit off her tongue. She might have doubled the price again and got it just as easily. But what an infernal humbug she was, I thought. She had drawn up no apprentice papers with General Scurlock.

"Then it's settled," Mr. Peacock said, and I could hear him rise from his chair. "You'll find me at the Black Horse Inn. I'll expect the boy tonight."

Mrs. Daggatt cleared her throat. "The money in advance, if you please."

28

"The money when you deliver the boy," he countered, and I could hear him stride toward the door.

"Mr. Peacock, may I ask why you insist upon Jingo and no other?"

His footsteps came to a stop and he must have turned to face her. I thought for a moment he wasn't going to answer. But then his voice hit me like a cannon shot.

"I'm his father," he said.

I might have fallen out of the chimney had I believed him. The man was a jolly rogue, but he didn't know my pa was a one-legged man.

He left, both heels clicking on the hardwood floor.

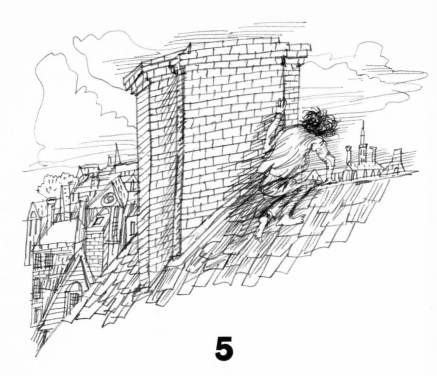

# 5

## CACTUS GOLD

Mrs. Daggatt must have sent for General Scurlock quick as lightning, for I saw him loping up the street like an answering clap of thunder.

I spied him from the roof. I had hoped to get a look at Mr. Jeffrey Peacock, Gent., before he departed, and had climbed the flue, but I was too late. I fancied he had driven off in a carriage with a fine span of horses. I remained aloft in the open air, thoughts tumbling about in my head and the whale's tooth in my pocket.

General Scurlock ducked in the back way and I reckoned Mrs. Daggatt would be waiting for him in her private parlor. I capered silently over the slate roof to her own chimney top. I thought I might lower myself for the entertainment of their conversation. Mrs. Daggatt would explode like a dropped pumpkin to learn that Mr. Peacock's two-hundred-dollar apprentice had slipped through General Scurlock's fingers.

But when I reached the chimney their voices came echoing up the flue. I stuck my head in. Tempers were clashing below and words rose like sparks on the updraft.

"You blundering, thick-skulled fool!" she roared. "You let the little brat run off?"

"Me dear Daggatt!" he protested.

"Don't dear Daggatt me! And hasn't the whale's tooth given you the slip as well!"

"A temporary embarrassment. A mere momentary setback. A bit o' patience is in order here, me dear Daggatt!"

"Patience! I promised to deliver the boy tonight!"

"Faugh! What's the gentleman's pittance to us once we lay hands on the scrimshaw? There's a treasure of cactus gold waiting for us in Mexico. I saw it with me own eyes, didn't I?"

"You were boozefuddled, the lot of you! Tavern tales, that's what it amounts to! I don't believe in the whale's tooth anymore'n I do that cactus gold."

Wasn't she trying to humbug him, I thought! *She* had the whale's tooth all along. Only *I* had it now and I'd be glad to see her face when she found it missing.

"Do ye take me for a jill-poke?" he thundered. "Didn't I trail little Billy Bottles soon as I was mustered out? And didn't I finally catch him up right here in Boston? And didn't I rattle his backbone and shake his teeth until he coughed up the old map?"

"Billy Bottles!" she scoffed.

"Aye, a weasel was Billy. But no worse than the rest of us, me dear Daggatt."

They kept up a windy clamor. I missed bits and pieces, but directly I began to get the gist of things. During the Mexico war, Scurlock and Billy Bottles and two or three others had stumbled across a peck of old coins hidden in a clump of cactus. Well, they weren't about to share out that minted gold with the whole U.S. Army. They hid it somewhere and planned to dig it up after the war.

But Scurlock and Bottles, being friends at the time, I reckon, had decided to fingle-fangle the others. They snuck out the cactus gold and buried it somewhere along the Mexico border. They drew a map, but then Bottles decided to fingle-fangle Scurlock himself. He popped the treasure in another spot while Scurlock was laid up with a bullet wound in the leg.

"Aye, that gold went leaping about like a Texas jack-rabbit," Scurlock was bellowing. "A buzzard could get lost in that country without a map. And our map wasn't

32

worth the cowhide I had drawn it on! But I had Billy by the throat, didn't I?"

"And you let him get away!"

"Was I to know he'd grown up a soot devil? But when I saw him snatch up a whale's tooth and shoot up the flue, didn't I put two and four together? He'd scrimshawed a new map and dodged me all over Boston like a chimney swallow. When he took a header down this very fireplace, didn't he call out me name and tell ye with his last cackling breath he'd left the whale's tooth chimney-hid? Aye, ye knew ye were on to something, me dear Daggatt! But ye needed *me* to discover what it was and ye bargained like a fishwife! Didn't we come to a partnership, open and fair and half and half on the treasure? And didn't I set myself up a sweepmaster with a flock of climbing boys to find it?"

"Numskull! He meant to send you on a fool's errand."

It was falling dark with great black clouds tumbling in from the sea. I remembered a rumpus in Mrs. Daggatt's parlor about a year before, but she'd told us it was only a thief caught and captured in the night. Billy Bottles!

I leaned my back against the chimney stack and examined the whale's tooth. I felt the first wild stirrings of treasure fever. But there wasn't enough light to make out the map.

I slipped it tight under the waistband of my breeches like a hidden pistol. Scurlock was no match for Mrs. Daggatt, I thought. *She had fingle-fangled him from the beginning!*

Billy Bottles must have had the scrimshaw *with* him when he fell. How else could she have got her claws on it?

Then she had flummoxed Scurlock with the story that the whale's tooth was chimney-hid. Maybe she expected him to give up the chase, for the tooth would likely be charred as the winter passed, and useless. In due time, by my reckoning, she intended to go venturing after that treasure by herself.

But Scurlock hadn't given up the chase. Before long he slammed out of the orphan house. I waited up in the night sky until he was well gone. Then I began easing myself down along the roof. I was burning to have a good look at that scrimshaw map.

But a slate shingle broke loose under me and my footing gave way. The shingle clattered to the ground and I slid like a hog on ice toward the cloud of elm branches along the edge of the roof. I tumbled into the tree, gulped a breath of air and slithered down the trunk. I meant to make a quick run for it.

I reached the ground. And there stood Mrs. Daggatt, her eyes ablaze and her hands out to grab me.

# 6

## THE MISSING FACES

The Black Horse Inn stood like a ship anchored and lantern-lit in the muddy darkness of the upper Post Road. A windy rain had come up. In a livery shay, and taking the reins herself, Mrs. Daggatt meant to deliver me in person. At our approach dogs came loping out of the stable yard to surround us, barking and whipping their tails about.

There was no danger of my jumping away. She had tied my thumbs behind my back with twine. The whale's tooth was still snugged and hidden under my shirt at the waist of my trousers. Now that we had arrived she undid my thumbs, and took me by the collar of my shirt. A tavern boy met us with a black cotton umbrella, but she held me out in the rain to wash the soot devil off me.

"Your father's here to fetch you," she wheezed. "A fine gentleman he is — better than you deserve. So you'll watch your tongue and say nothing about being put out to scraping chimneys."

When she judged I was washed clean enough, clothes and all, she marched me into the Black Horse Inn. The

public room was a bright, cheery place with great wooden beams and a creaky floor. Men and dogs were warming themselves at the open fireplace. They glanced at me as if I were a half-drowned cat.

It didn't take Mrs. Daggatt long to spy out Jeffrey Peacock, Gent. He was seated alone, reading a newspaper in the far corner and smoking a long clay pipe. A tankard stood at his elbow.

He didn't bother to look up even as we approached. I had conjured up a peacock of a man with a stolen ring or two blazing from his fingers. But there was nothing foppish about him. Mr. Peacock was taller'n a stackpole, with his legs stretched out and crossed on an opposite chair. His glistening jackboots looked a yard long. His coat hung from his shoulders like a cape and his white shirt stood open at the neck. Chestnut hair curled and tumbled gloomily over his forehead and down his neck. He had the air of a weary traveler who had yet to reach his destination, or maybe had no destination at all.

"Ah, there you are, Mr. Peacock," Mrs. Daggatt said with a sudden gust of smiles. "And see here who I've brought along — your very own son! Isn't he the spittin' image? I see it now myself. Indeed, I can, Mr. Peacock!"

He gazed up from his paper. Slowly, he arched one eyebrow and fixed her with an icy blue-eyed stare.

"I beg your pardon, madam?"

"It's your son, Mr. Peacock."

"What the devil are you talking about?"

"My dear sir! It's two hundred dollars we agreed upon."

He hadn't so much as whisked me a glance. "How do you know he's my son?"

"Tush, Mr. Peacock, you said so yourself. This afternoon, at the orphanage."

"Do you believe every posturing, brazen-faced stranger who walks through your door?"

Her face began to swell and redden. "I mistook you for a gentleman," she scowled.

"That's a pity."

Oh, he was a rare one, I thought!

"Do you want the little guttersnipe, or don't you?" she crackled.

"What's this? You sell your orphans like poultry?" For the first time his eyes slid over to me. "He looks like you dragged him from the river, madam."

"You can have him for a hundred. A hundred dollars, Mr. Peacock, and let's be done with it."

"What's your name, lad?"

"Jingo," I said. I earnestly hoped he'd take me.

"Is that the name you were instructed to say?"

"No, sir," I answered. "I've been Jingo long as I can recollect."

"Jingo what?"

"Jingo Hawks, sir."

"How long have you been at the orphanage?"

"Seven *infernal* years, sir," I replied. A wrathy hiss escaped Mrs. Daggatt's lips.

"Would it take your fancy to go traveling with me, lad?"

"Yes, *sir,* Mr. Peacock."

He tossed a leather pouch on the table and turned to Mrs. Daggatt. "There's your two hundred dollars, madam." And he picked up his newspaper and resumed reading as if she had ceased to exist.

She snatched up the pouch, turned on her heels and went rumbling and grumbling out. It was a momentous occasion. I felt nearly light-headed to see the last of her. Mr. Peacock was a strange one, and maybe I was bought and paid for, but I was free of the orphan house forever!

Suddenly he tossed the newspaper to the floor and burst into dark, angry laughter. I was taken by surprise and stood open-eyed and stock-still.

"The old harpy!" he said. "Greedy as a muckworm. I took her measure the moment I cast eyes on her. *Tush! Glory be!* What fawning rubbish."

I wiped a trickle of rainwater off the tip of my nose, and stared at him.

"But we gave her a little of her own back, didn't we? She squirmed like an eel when she thought I'd send her packing empty-handed."

"You were almighty generous, sir," I said, hesitantly. His eyes seemed to be avoiding me. "Mrs. Daggatt would have settled for ten dollars. Less, even."

"It's shabby for a man not to honor his word," he stated flatly. And then the dark shadows lifted from his face. He laughed again, shifting his glance, and took my measure.

"You do look like a guttersnipe, don't you, Jango?"

"Jingo, sir," I said. "My name's Jingo."

"You're scrawny as a cat-stick. Don't you eat?"

"When I can."

"Innkeeper!" he called.

But it was the landlord's wife who came rustling over. She was a brisk, smiling little woman with cheeks shiny as porcelain. "Yes, Mr. Hemlock!"

My eyebrows shot up smartly. Hemlock?

"Dry this lad's clothes by the fire," he said. "Take him to my room and have a hot supper brought up to him."

"The poor tyke," she sighed, melting at the scruffy sight of me. "Is he run away from home?"

"Surely you can see the spittin' image, my good lady," he answered, relighting the long clay pipe. "He's my long lost son."

"Lamb o' the Lord!"

"Have my account drawn up. We'll be leaving first thing in the morning."

I was led up a narrow flight of stairs to a corner room. I withdrew the whale's tooth and stripped off my wet clothes in the dark. I handed them out the door to the innkeeper's wife and lit a candle. I saw two vast beds under a low ceiling and blank canvas in gold frames stacked along the walls.

I jumped into bed to wait for my supper. I began to examine the whale's tooth in the candlelight, even though my thoughts kept wandering. Mr. Peacock had turned into Mr. Hemlock. A swindler for sure, I thought. What use did he have for me?

I kept gazing at the whale's tooth, but could hardly

40

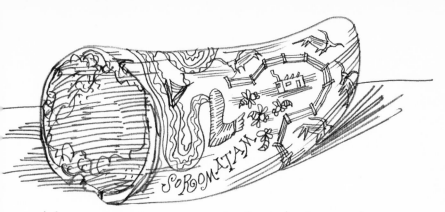

cipher a proper treasure map in the scrimshaw carvings.
I made out a river with a small boat afloat on it, a swarm
of bees or hornets, a man's elbow, several oxen with enormous long horns and a fence wandering around a strange
flat-roofed house with a crooked chimney pipe. But there
*was* a mysterious word carved like lace in the bone:

## SOROMATAM

I pondered the signs, but it didn't help much. And then
I calculated that Billy Bottles had been everlasting clever
about it. Maybe he wanted to be sure that his cactus gold
map didn't *look* like a map.

I decided not to bother my head about it. There were
those blank frames against the walls, and the man's bluff
that he was my father. I wondered how I fit into any
swindle he was about. Finally I hid the scrimshaw under
my pillow, took hold of the candle and got out of bed.

I crossed the room to the stacks of canvas. The gold
frames glistened. And then I realized they were wrong
side out.

I turned one over and saw a painting of a lady, from

the waist up, in the grandest finery. But it gave me a start. The woman had no face. None at all.

Quickly, I began turning other pictures about. The finery was different, but one thing was the same. Every confounded painting was faceless — blank and white as an egg!

# 7

## FINGLE-FANGLED

We were on the road at daybreak. The rainstorm had passed, leaving puddles scattered about like broken glass.

Mr. Peacock-Hemlock traveled by private coach. Sitting beside him I felt that I had come up wondrously in the world. But he was neither a gentleman, I decided, nor a judge of horseflesh.

He had no coachman. He took the reins himself. The coach was an old thing, with great creaking wheels and two nags to pull it. They shambled along like plow horses.

He shook the reins from time to time to keep the animals from dozing off. The inside of the coach was piled helter-skelter with pots, pans, sacks of oats, boxes, blankets and the ghostly paintings of faceless ladies. They fairly boggled the mind.

Mr. Peacock-Hemlock had hardly uttered a word to me since the night before and I kept my thoughts to myself. But I thought some midnight darkness occupied his head; it stood me well to be on guard. And I thought some horse trader had most certainly got the best of him in those flea-bitten coach horses.

43

We rode along in silence. The tall coach wheels sliced along the muddy road without once bogging down. The sun warmed our backs and suddenly Mr. Peacock-Hemlock, or whatever his name might be, broke into a whistling tune.

"You don't talk much, do you, lad?" he said with a sudden grin.

I was caught up short. But glimpsing his smile I calculated he was only trying to cast off his brooding silence.

"I do well enough on occasion, sir," I answered.

"You need a pair of boots."

"They'd only get muddy," I said, though I wished I had a fine pair of jackboots to stride about in, like his own. "What do you call your animals?"

"The off-horse is named Billygoat. The one on the left is Sunflower."

I began to feel easier in his company. "I imagine you had to do a lot of clever trading to find gentle animals like that. Slower'n stock-still, I mean."

"Slow!" he erupted, laughing, and the tree branches seemed to shake. "Why, Jango, they're *racehorses*, both of them."

If he had a touch of madness, I thought, he was being mortal good-humored about it. "My name's Jingo, sir."

"Have you ever driven a coach before?"

"No, sir."

He handed me the reins. "All you have to do is hold the beasts in check. Otherwise they'll take off like a streak and we'll be clear to the Mississippi before sundown."

44

His long, booted legs stretched out like stovepipes, and he pulled his hat down over his forehead. I gripped the reins tightly and suddenly felt years older driving that coach. I wondered if that was why he had brought me along — to train me up as his coachman. Well, that would suit me fine!

"Where we heading?" I asked.

I waited for an answer, but he didn't answer, so I didn't ask again. I calculated he had his own secrets and I'd better not pry.

The coach went wee-wawing through the mud. If Billygoat and Sunflower were racehorses I'd be glad to go dashing after the cactus gold. The whale's tooth, snugged inside my shirt, was my own secret and I decided to keep it to myself.

He started whistling again and my thoughts went skittering over the thumping mysteries of the day before. Finally, I decided to chance a few questions while he was in an uncommon good mood.

"Sir, how come you turned up looking especially for me at the orphan house? By name, I mean?"

He didn't answer. He just went on whistling.

"You're not my pa," I stated.

His blue eyes shifted under the brim of his hat. "Obviously," he stated right back.

"But you pretended to Mrs. Daggatt."

"You're free to run off anytime you choose," he answered, which was no answer at all.

Now it was my turn to fall silent. I didn't want to run

45

off. Not while I could sit high and important on the coach seat and drive that span of horses. I wondered if that was why he had turned the reins over to me. He was devilish smart.

He crossed his legs and gazed at the road ahead. "You recollect your father, don't you, lad?"

"Yes, sir."

"Well enough to pick him out in a crowd?"

"Yes, sir," I said. "He's a one-legged man with teeth blacker'n tar. A cutthroat, most likely."

"Splendid," he muttered. "You can help me find the scoundrel."

My heart dropped a notch or two. Mr. Peacock-Hemlock meant to use me to spy out my pa — *that* was the reason he had fetched me from the orphan house.

I felt fiercely disappointed. I felt fingle-fangled. The

last man alive I wanted to go searching for was my pa. I'd as soon stick my head in a beehive as shake his confounded hand. He'd abandoned me to the orphan house and I didn't intend to forgive him — not in a thousand years.

"We'll keep a sharp eye out for a one-legged man," Mr. Peacock-Hemlock said.

I clamped my jaws shut. He'd wake up one morning and find me gone in a burnt hurry. He was not more than a cut above Mrs. Daggatt and General Dirty-Face Jim Scurlock, I decided. They were a pestiferous lot, all of them, turning me to their own advantage.

I simmered for a considerable time. It didn't once occur to Mr. Peacock-Hemlock that I might have contrary feelings in the matter. As far as he was concerned I was bought and paid for.

But slowly my thoughts began to turn around. I thought of the scrimshaw map and the cactus gold and pondered a way to fingle-fangle things to my own liking.

"No, sir," I remarked finally. "No sense in looking. You won't spy out my pa around here."

"Are you sure?"

"Certain." I stared straight ahead. "I know for a fact that he lit out for the Mexico border. Still there, most likely."

That was a howling lie, but he answered it with a casual gesture of his hand. "Then that's where we'll head. Mexico it is, Jango."

And he picked up whistling again.

He could look for my pa till doomsday, I thought. I meant to look for that cactus gold.

# 8

## CAPTAIN DAYLIGHT

Three days passed before we met our first highwayman.

Billygoat and Sunflower ambled along like sleepwalkers, putting mile after muddy mile between us and Boston. At the rate we creaked along I expected to be full grown before we reached the Mexico border.

And Mr. Peacock-Hemlock delayed us at every crossroad. He'd step down as if to stretch his legs, but that wasn't what he was up to. Sometimes he would scatter fresh grass like a green ribbon between the ruts of the road. Other times he'd set a stick at the crossroads — always a long one with a stub left on.

If he had a touch of madness I wasn't anxious to tangle with it. I didn't ask questions. And I hadn't a notion why he was on the trail of my pa. It was clear enough that if Mr. Peacock-Hemlock wanted me to know a thing, he'd tell me.

But as the days went by, sharp and clear, curiosity got the best of me. "Them cat-sticks supposed to hold off evil spirits, sir?"

49

To my surprise he answered straight out. "I'm setting a gypsy trail."

"Gypsies?" I must have gaped at him. "Are you a gypsy gentleman?"

He was polishing the gold head of his walking stick. But I don't think it was gold. I suspicioned it was brass. "No," he answered quietly.

And that's when we came upon the highwayman.

He sat on horseback at the crossroads brandishing a pair of pistols at a buggy. I hauled back on the reins.

"What are you stopping for?" Mr. Peacock-Hemlock asked.

"Robbers!"

"I only see one. Drive on."

I swallowed hard and shook the reins. No doubt about it, I thought. Mr. Peacock-Hemlock was thatchy in the head. He'd get us both shot full of holes.

We pulled up to the buggy and he said, "Excuse me, gentlemen. You're blocking the road. Kindly pull to one side, like good fellows, and get on with your business."

The highwayman shifted his eyes to us in the wildest amazement. And he shifted his pistols as well.

"Stand and deliver!" he scowled. He was a blunt-nosed man with tangled hair and rings on all his fingers.

"Deliver what?" said Mr. Peacock-Hemlock with the utmost unconcern.

"Bust yur haslet!" the highwayman exploded. "Do you think I'm standing here to collect yur linen! Gold, man! Yur watch and jewels! Deliver!"

50

You'd think Mr. Peacock-Hemlock had gone deaf. "I declare, sir, those dueling pistols take my eye. Handsome as I ever saw. They do you credit."

"Deliver, you pesky fool!"

All the while the man in the buggy sat trembling and washing his hands with worry. He was a smallish man in a black frock coat that hung as loose on him as a shirt on a beanpole.

"Well, sir," said Mr. Peacock-Hemlock, "if you intend to rob me I'll have to insist upon a small favor."

"I'll favor you with a window in yur skull!" replied the highwayman.

"No, thank you kindly," Mr. Peacock-Hemlock smiled, climbing down from the coach. "You see I'm carrying a considerable sum. Unfortunately, it doesn't entirely belong to me. I have a partner and I'm afraid he'd never believe I was robbed in broad daylight on a public road."

"Deliver, I say!"

"In due time, sir." Mr. Peacock-Hemlock threw open one of the coach doors. "Now if you would be generous enough to put a bullet through the door I could hardly be accused of deceit. Evidence, sir. Surely a ball of lead is a fair exchange for a hundred times its weight in gold."

The highwayman burst into a laugh and fired. The coach door rattled on its hinges with a hole shot clean through it.

"That's a good chap," said Mr. Peacock-Hemlock. "Now the other door, sir. I intend to make a fine story of it, I assure you. You'll be famous in twenty-four hours. If I'm not mistaken you'll be whispered about as the most daring lone swift-nick of the road. You'll be remembered in the same glorious company with Captain Thunderbolt and Captain Lightfoot. A name. You'll need a name, sir. How does 'Captain Daylight' strike you?"

The highwayman fired through the other coach door and puffed up like a turkey. "Aye, Captain Daylight it is!"

"Now, if you'll just put a ball through my hat we'll be done with it." Mr. Peacock-Hemlock ambled closer. "But do miss my scalp, won't you?"

"Great keezer's ghost!" the highwayman declared. "I've discharged both pistols."

"That *is* unfortunate," Mr. Peacock-Hemlock answered, and struck forward like a shaft of lightning. He gave the horse a sharp prod with his walking stick, the horse reared and Captain Daylight was thrown sprawling in the mud. He rose in time to meet the swing of Mr. Peacock-Hemlock's jackboot, which must have filled his head with birdsong.

*"Chavo,"* Mr. Peacock-Hemlock called to me. "Fetch a bit of rawhide from the coach."

I hopped to it, and in no time Captain Daylight was trussed hand and foot. Mr. Peacock-Hemlock threw him across the saddle like a sack of flour and tied the horse to the rear of the buggy.

Then he turned to the nervous little man who had watched it all. "Take this empty-headed rascal to the nearest constable."

"Bless you, sir," the man piped up. "I do believe he

meant to kill me before you came along. He was in a terrible rage when all I had on my person was a dollar and twenty-eight cents."

Mr. Peacock-Hemlock grinned. "I don't have even that small sum left in my pouch. The inns and tollgates have bankrupted me."

I was perplexed to hear that. I had come to believe that Mr. Peacock-Hemlock was a man of vast means.

"Here is my card," said the frock-coated man, who had got over his fear and trembling. "If you are ever in Deerfield and I can be of service, please call on me."

Mr. Peacock-Hemlock gazed at the card and smiled. "Thank you, Reverend Pye. You have already done me a splendid service. Good-bye, sir."

It was only after we parted that I caught my breath from the encounter, and stopped to wonder what splendid service the Reverend Pye had performed by remaining perched like a crow in his buggy.

And then, like a distant echo coming back to me, the word *chavo* sounded in my head. Hadn't Mr. Peacock-Hemlock called me that, as if my name had slipped his mind in the excitement of the moment?

*Chavo.* It was part of my secret language, like *mishto* and *hatchi-witchu.* It was a word from long ago.

How had *he* known it?

These bafflers occupied my thoughts while Mr. Peacock-Hemlock sat beside me on the box, whistling to himself. I had to admit that he had been uncommon clever in dealing with the highwayman. Some hours later I spied fresh trouble ahead.

"We're coming to a tollgate," I said.

"Drive on," he answered.

"But you said you were bankrupt. They won't let us through without paying the toll."

"Forward, lad."

We slowed to a halt at the wooden gate across the road. A man with sagging eyes came out of the gatehouse, spit tobacco juice and touched his cap. He looked more of a villain than Captain Daylight.

"Sixty cents for the coach, gents. Eighteen cents each for the horses. Pays to keep up the roads, y'know."

I hadn't noticed that the road was kept up at all. It was two boggy ruts. And as I glanced at the rates painted and weathered on the signboard I saw that he meant to overcharge us. I was about to open my mouth when Mr. Peacock-Hemlock passed the toll keeper the Rev. Pye's card.

"Another," the man muttered with clear disappointment, and returned the card. "Another preacher, is it?"

He swung the gate open, we passed through and continued on our way.

"He meant to charge you double for the coach," I said.

"You'll soon learn the ways of the road, Jango," Mr. Peacock-Hemlock laughed. "If our fortunes don't improve we'll travel the toll roads clear to Mexico on the good reverend's card. Men of the cloth pass toll-free, as you saw."

"The name's *Jingo,* sir," I said once more. There seemed no getting it fixed properly in his mind.

"*Jingo,* of course," he replied. "I expect I had better replenish our funds. You really must have a decent pair of boots."

"You called me *chavo,* sir, a while back. What nature of word is that?" And then I added as innocently as I could, "I declare if it doesn't sound Mohawk."

He began filling his clay pipe. "It means *lad,"* he answered simply, "in the gypsy language."

A thunderclap couldn't have surprised me more. I fell silent — wondering if I were gypsy-born.

# 9

# AT THE RED JACKET INN

When night fell we were still on the road. Well past suppertime we approached a village. I could smell it before we saw the first light. Chimneys charged the air with the cozy scent of woodsmoke.

The stars were clouding over and it was likely to rain again. But I didn't calculate we'd be stopping for the night. We didn't have a tormented cent between us. It wouldn't surprise me if we shared oats with the horses, and I was hungry enough.

The village stood huddled against the dark around a marshy green. Mr. Peacock-Hemlock took it in with a single glance. Then he pointed to the brightly painted sign of the Red Jacket Inn. "I believe we'll put up there for a few days," he said. "It looks a prosperous place, doesn't it?"

"But, sir —"

"Pull in, Jango."

I did what I was told, but felt mighty uneasy about it.

They'd put the law on us when they discovered we had no money.

A stable boy took the coach and I followed Mr. Peacock-Hemlock into the public room. He carried himself like he meant to buy the place, and began issuing orders almost before the innkeeper could greet us.

"Your finest accommodations, sir," he said. "Supper as soon as possible. Mock turtle soup, boiled mutton with caper sauce and oyster patties if you have nothing better at hand. Is there a cobbler in the village? Have him call on us at once. A mug of flip while I'm waiting and fresh milk for the lad."

"Indeed, sir," the inkeeper smiled. He was a cheery red-faced man named Foxhall with a cheery red-haired wife. "Maggie, my love," he said, catching her eye. "Room Nine and see there's a warm fire. Send Finch for the cobbler." And then he turned back to Mr. Peacock-Hemlock. "Now, sir, if you'll kindly sign the register Mr. . . . Mr. . . ."

"Jones, sir. My card. Charles Balthazar Jones, *artiste extraordinaire.*"

My eyes must have spun in my head. He had a card for every occasion!

He signed the register with a flourish. "And have my canvases and paint box brought in from the coach. I may do a bit of daubing to pass the time."

"Immediately, sir," replied the innkeeper, who appeared pleased to have a man of importance on the premises.

I watched the serving girl stick the end of a red-hot

57

poker into the mug of flip to warm it, and soon Mr. Pea-cock-Hemlock-Jones had taken command of a wing chair near the fireplace.

"I could scrape chimneys in the morning," I said.

"Chimneys! What the devil for?"

"We'll need to earn a hatful of money, sir. Mrs. Dag-gatt was having me trained up to be a climbing boy."

He turned with a sudden scowl to gaze at the fire. "A climbing boy! Drink your milk, *chavo*." A moment later he broke into a grin. Then he slipped me a wink. "We're beginning to earn all the money we'll need as we sit here."

Either I was traveling with a madman or the most auda-cious humbug on the road. The workings of his mind were beyond me. I suspected he had lived among gypsies and it wouldn't surprise me if he was up to some gypsy trick.

It seemed no time at all before the cobbler turned up. He was a short, bull-necked man named Pratt. He traced around my foot on a piece of newspaper while Mr. Pea-cock-Hemlock-Jones looked through his samples of leather.

"Does this black calfskin take your fancy, Jango?"

"No, sir," I answered. I'd feel too infernal dressed up. "But I do like that buckskin."

"Then buckskin it is, Mr. Pratt. And kindly allow grow-ing room in the toes."

The cobbler nodded. "I'll have boots on the lad's feet tomorrow."

"Capital," Mr. Peacock-Hemlock-Jones said, and re-turned to his hot flip.

We were sitting down to supper when the stable boy began packing in the faceless paintings. It didn't surprise me that they caused a stir. I filled my mouth as quickly as I could before we got booted out. Mr. Foxhall would be sure to see that he had taken in some barmy variety of traveler.

But Mrs. Foxhall's eyes lit up and the serving girls joined her in a cluster around the paintings. Everyone began to babble. I kept stuffing my mouth.

"Have you ever seen such lovely dresses?" I heard the innkeeper's wife sigh. "And look at that lace collar! Why, it appears positively real!"

Mr. Peacock-Hemlock-Jones continued eating at a leisurely pace. "Excellent venison, sir," he commented to Mr. Foxhall. But the landlord had turned to join his wife. The pictures drew people from every corner of the inn and they buzzed from one to the other like flies.

I wondered if they had all gone blind! Didn't they notice there wasn't a face to be found on any of the paintings? Why the fuss over dresses and lace collars?

The next thing I knew the innkeeper had stationed himself beside us. "You are indeed an *artiste extraordinaire,* sir. Pictures without faces! Is that the latest fashion in Boston?"

"The boiled potatoes are splendid," Mr. Peacock-Hemlock-Jones replied.

"My dear sir —"

We were in for a snarl now, I thought. But Mr. Peacock-Hemlock-Jones rose from the table, ignoring the

59

innkeeper, and strode toward the chattering women.

"Madam," he said to Mrs. Foxhall. "Will you kindly select the painting of your choice."

"Oh, the one with the yellow dress, Mr. Jones. Is it from Paris?"

He lifted the frame and propped it across the arms of a chair. He brought an oil lamp closer, seated her opposite him, opened his paint box and set to work.

He began painting in red hair and snapping bright eyes and busied himself with the exact little smile that played about our landlady's lips. I had never seen anything so wondrous fast and clever.

Perhaps an hour had passed when the innkeeper declared, "My dear Maggie, it's become the very image of you!"

Mr. Peacock-Hemlock-Jones kept daubing away in a burnt hurry. Finally he spoke with a brush clamped between his teeth. "Do you have a favorite brooch, Mrs. Foxhall?"

"I'll fetch your cameo," said the innkeeper. But then he stopped short. "Mr. Jones, I do hope your fee is not beyond our reach."

"There will be no fee, sir."

He was daft, I thought! We hadn't so much as a penny with a hole in it and he was going to make a gift of the picture.

"Well, sir," answered the innkeeper, his face aglow. "You're no businessman — I can see that. You're welcome to the Red Jacket as long as you care to favor us with your society. If you think you can best me in a contest of generosity you're mistaken." And off he went to fetch the brooch.

At least we would be eating, I thought. And the landlord wouldn't be putting the law on us. I couldn't help admiring Mr. Peacock-Hemlock-Jones' lofty confidence. Perhaps he wasn't so much a lunatic as an odd stick.

I watched him brush in a cameo at Mrs. Foxhall's neck, and the portrait was finished. The faceless painting now had a face. The innkeeper immediately hung it on the wall, and everyone stood back to gaze at it. By that time I was so tired and sleepy I could hardly keep my eyes open. Mr. Peacock-Hemlock-Jones returned to his dinner, grown cold.

"Go to bed, *chavo*."

"Are you a famous artist, sir?" I asked.

He grinned. "No. Just a traveler of the roads. When winter sets in I paint a supply of grand ladies in the latest styles. Once the roads thaw I gypsy about filling in the faces of farm wives and villagers, as you saw."

"Are you a gypsy, sir?"

He didn't bother to look up from his plate. "I told you. No. But you are, lad. Your name's not Jingo. It's Jango. Spelled with a *D*. Django."

And he called for another hot flip.

I carried a candlestick to our room and once behind the closed door I studied myself in the mirror over the shaving cabinet. I looked into my eyes as if I'd never seen them before — gypsy eyes. And my hair tumbled about in dark gypsy curls. And I smiled what I hoped might be a gypsy smile, a crafty, wicked, one-eyed smile.

I *liked* being a gypsy! It was first rate and a half. Maybe I'd put a ring in my ear and learn to tell the future and all manner of gypsy things. I kept posturing in front of the mirror, feeling a half-stranger to myself.

Finally I hid the whale's tooth under the pillow and crawled into bed. It would take some getting used to — being gypsy born. I hoped Mr. Peacock-Hemlock-Jones wasn't playing some confounded trick on me. I was tired of being a puzzle to myself.

# 10

## THE SCRIMSHAW MAP

Mr. Peacock-Hemlock-Jones was a late sleeper and a sly fox. I used up the morning poking around, never suspecting that his name was jumping about the village like a flea in a glove.

When I returned to the Red Jacket at noon Mr. Foxhall's face was lit up like a lamp. "See there who's come to call," he chuckled, nodding toward several men waiting impatiently for Mr. Peacock-Hemlock-Jones to come down. "That's Judge Stockbridge chewing his cigar. His wife has told him not to return without the *artiste extraordinaire*. And the same for Doc Holliway warming his coattails at the fire." He rattled off a few other names and added, "That's just the beginning, mark my word."

It didn't take me long to reason out why Mr. Peacock-Hemlock-Jones had favored our landlady with a portrait. When the villagers awoke to the news that the innkeeper's wife had had her picture painted, the judge's wife must have sputtered with envy. I reckoned the doctor's wife didn't want to be outdone by the judge's wife and had

64

shuffled her husband off to make sure that she got *her*
picture painted as well.

Even as I stood there the village banker came glowering
in, followed by a country squire and an army colonel in
full uniform.

When Mr. Peacock-Hemlock-Jones made his appearance
the husbands surrounded him like a pack of hounds, all
yelping at once. He silenced them with a hand. "Gentlemen, please," he said. "Allow me to order my breakfast
and then, I regret to say, we must travel on."

There was a great, mortal groan from the men, who would have to face their wives.

But Mr. Foxhall had his wits about him. "I'm sure," he said, "that we can prevail upon Mr. Jones to enjoy our hospitality a few days longer, gentlemen — if the price is satisfactory."

Quicker than you could count to two he appointed himself our business advisor and while Mr. Peacock-Hemlock-Jones sat down to a late meal he collected the portrait fees in advance.

"Thunder and fury!" exclaimed Mr. Peacock-Hemlock-Jones when the harvest of greenbacks and gold pieces was set before him. "I suppose I have no confounded choice but to delay our departure!"

I knew he had planned all along to remain. Oh, he was slick as an apple seed, I thought! He was not a man to offer his talents like a common peddler. Folks had turned up, hat in hand, to beg *him* for the favor of his services.

It was early afternoon before he made his first call. I followed along, carrying faceless ladies under each arm. I began to feel uneasy about fingle-fangling him into striking out for the Mexico border. Despite myself, I was coming to like him. He was dreadfully independent and considerable smart. I puffed up just walking about in his shadow.

We returned to the Red Jacket by early candlelight and the cobbler was waiting with a pair of buckskin boots. My heart leaped a beat or two. I thought I had never seen such an everlasting fine pair of boots. I could hardly be-

66

lieve they were meant for me. They had the fresh, new smell of tanner's oil.

"How do they fit, *chavo?*"

"Capital, sir," I smiled.

Mr. Peacock-Hemlock-Jones nodded and paid the cobbler. Then he ordered a hot flip for himself and another glass of fresh milk for me.

I passed most of the evening strutting about in the boots and wishing I could see myself in them. I went upstairs and down, and wandered about prouder'n a game rooster. They made me feel that I was somebody else.

Then I stopped to realize that I *was* somebody else. I wasn't one of Mrs. Daggatt's orphan house brats anymore. My name wasn't Jingo — it was Django. And I was a gypsy.

When I finally went up to bed I couldn't bring myself to pull off the boots. I'd sleep in them. For all I knew gypsies always slept in their boots.

I wondered how Mr. Peacock-Hemlock-Jones came to know so much about me. He couldn't have learned things from my pa. If he had ever met my pa he wouldn't need me along to spy him out. No, sir. They had never met. And yet he was trailing my pa like a bloodhound.

I reasoned there was some fury between them — revenge, most likely. I knew better than to ask Mr. Peacock-Hemlock-Jones about it, or anything else. He kept his thoughts tighter'n a fist.

He might be an odd stick, but I was coming to feel closer to him than any man in sight. He never ordered me about like an orphan. I was certain he had noticed the whale's tooth I kept tucked away, but he asked no questions.

I began to feel dreadful uncomfortable about leading him on a wild goose chase. He was never going to find my pa along the Mexico border, and I was tempted to tell him the truth.

I withdrew the whale's tooth and studied the scrimshaw markings. I'd be content to go gypsying about with Mr. Peacock-Hemlock-Jones and maybe we'd find the treasure. And then maybe he'd forgive me.

But maybe he wouldn't, I thought. I was sorry he ever had trusted me. Now he had me fitted out in spandy new boots and I was repaying him with a monstrous lie. I began to worry that he'd freeze up and tell me to make a straight shirttail out of his sight.

I was mulling things over when he walked in.

"Still awake, Django?" he asked.

"I'm not sleepy, sir."

"Boots don't belong in bed."

"A body can't be too precious careful with thieves and scoundrels about," I said. "I reckon I'd better keep them on day and night."

He laughed, standing with his back to the fireplace, and I could tell he took as much pleasure in the buckskins as I did. I wanted to thank him, but the words stuck to my tongue.

"They'll last you clear to Mexico and back," he said.

My mind made itself up, and I began pulling off the

boots. "Sir," I muttered softly, "I don't reckon you'll want me to keep these."

"What are you talking about?"

"I humbugged you. I don't have a notion where my pa is. I made that up about his being somewhere along the Mexico border."

He stood silently for a long time. I felt myself wither up under his blue-eyed gaze.

"Nonsense," he snapped finally. "You didn't humbug me. You were telling the truth."

"No, sir."

He turned away with a fierce scrowl. "What mischief is this? If you have tired of my company, *chavo*, you're free to go your own way. It's not necessary to make up lies."

Somehow he was getting everything mixed up. I didn't want to leave him. "I'm not lying *now*," I replied earnestly. "I was lying *before!*"

He shot me a baffled look. "But your pa *is* most certainly to be found in Mexico. I have been aware of that all along. If you'd told me he was in Canada you'd have sent me on a fool's errand. I'd have been infernally put out with you."

Suddenly *I* was feeling muddled. My pa in Mexico after all? It couldn't be.

"But, sir —"

"Take my word for it. We'll find him."

"But I don't *want* to find him," I blurted out.

"I can't blame you for that. If you did indeed try to humbug me you must have had good reason."

69

I took a deep breath. "Yes, sir. There's treasure in Mexico and I wanted to go after it."

A smile began to kindle itself in his eyes. "Treasure?"

"And I've got the map. It's carved in this whale's tooth."

"Then we've both a reason to go to Mexico, haven't we?" He began pulling off his coat and seemed to dismiss the matter.

"Don't you want to see the map?" I asked anxiously.

"Decidedly not. It's entirely your affair."

"But there's gold enough for both of us," I said quickly. "We could go partners."

"Partners fall out. No, *chavo*. I have riches enough in that paint box. A man's skills make up a splendid treasure and he needn't fear having them looted."

I began to feel a little desperate. Partners might fall out, but we wouldn't, I assured myself. It would ease my conscience if he'd go shares with me. I was mortal sorry that I had tried to fingle-fangle him. He'd managed to turn things about, somehow, but it only increased my desperation. Mrs. Daggatt would have obliged me with a thrashing and I would still be stretching the truth to my own fancy. But now I was determined to finish with that brand of mischief.

"The trouble is," I said softly, "I can't exactly make sense of my map. I'd be eternally grateful if you'd take a look, sir."

He held out his hand and I leaped out of bed with the whale's tooth. I carried the lamp closer while he began examining the scrimshaw. River and hornets and the

70

man's elbow. I told him how I had come by it and finally he said, "A ranch house with a fence around it hardly seems a proper treasure map, does it?"

"No, sir."

"But notice the cattle grazing here and there."

"I did."

"Look at this longhorn steer. It's tied to a corner post. That's highly irregular."

"Is it?" I began to feel a rising excitement. But there was still the word deeply scratched into the tooth: SORO-MATAM. That was highly irregular, too.

He studied it for a full minute and then jumped up. "Carry the lamp over here," he grinned, leading me to the mirror over the shaving cabinet.

When he held the whale's tooth to the mirror everything reversed itself, and the word still came out irregular.

"Matamoros," I muttered, reading it off the glass. "It still doesn't say anything.

"On the contrary, Django," he replied, and I could tell he was pleased with himself. "It's a Mexican town near the mouth of the Rio Grande — notice the river. I've been there twice. All you've got to do is locate this exact ranch house somewhere out of Matamoros, dig under the north-west corner post where you see the longhorn tied, and if you don't haul up treasure someone got there first."

He handed the whale's tooth back to me. I was stunned by the speed in which he had figured it out.

"Now put your boots back on," he grinned. "In case you walk in your sleep."

# 11

## THE DREADFUL VISITOR

Matamoros! Now that I knew the treasure spot I was in a whirlwind hurry to be up and gone. But Mr. Peacock-Hemlock-Jones appeared to have dismissed the entire matter from his thoughts. We lingered on at the Red Jacket Inn while he went about his affairs.

I cooled my heels as best I could. Travelers came and went, including a fat man who engraved the Lord's Prayer on the heads of pins. He created a great stir. The writing was so wondrously fine you couldn't see it with the naked eye, and he did a brisk business in pins and magnifying glasses.

I thought the day would never pass, nor the next. Of course I paraded about in my buckskin boots, new breeches, a hickory shirt and a sheepskin jerkin. Mr. Peacock-Hemlock-Jones had had my orphan house rags burned as he replaced them, piece by piece.

"You'll cut a splendid figure on the frontier," he remarked at supper.

"No, sir," I muttered. "I expect to grow out of my clothes before we leave the Red Jacket Inn."

He laughed. "We'll take our departure soon."

"When?"

"Tomorrow morning," he said, and my spirits took a mighty leap.

I left him smoking his clay pipe before the fire. I helped myself to a candlestick from the rack behind the innkeeper's counter and made my way upstairs. I meant to be awake and ready to travel at first light. I hoped he wouldn't stay up half the night and sleep till noon.

A wind had come up. I could hear a shutter banging somewhere and the inn creaked in all its joints. When I stepped through the bedroom door a sudden draft snuffed out the flame of my candle. I reckoned I had left the window open.

But almost in the same instant a hand clapped itself across my mouth, the door was kicked shut behind me and my hair must have shot up like the quills of a porcupine.

"Not a sound, ye cheeky little savage!"

I recognized the voice at once and my heart dropped like a well bucket.

It was General Dirty-Face Jim Scurlock.

"So ye found the chimney-hid thing, did ye?" he laughed softly. "Aye, and ain't ye overjoyed to see me?"

I heard him cock a pistol and then I felt the barrel cold against the side of my head.

"Handy it over, ye pesky little maggot. The whale's tooth! Daggatt spliced two and four together and we know ye took it. Sleeping in her chimney, were ye? Aye, she

73

found the evidence and the scrimshaw gone. She thought to double-deal me, but came to her proper senses. Oh, you and that tall gent was easy to follow. Now, where be it, eh? Speak up!"

I made a few throat sounds and it occurred to him to ease off with his hand.

"Well?"

I swallowed a gulp of air and tried to catch my wits. If I could stall him long enough maybe Mr. Peacock-Hemlock-Jones would come striding in and I figured he was a match for anyone — even General Dirty-Face Jim Scurlock.

"You promised a ten dollar gold piece reward," I said. "Indeed you did, sir."

His temper shot to a boil. "I'll reward ye with an extra hole in your head!" He took my neck in one fist and began shaking me like a rattle. "Answer up, ye ungrateful, tricksy little brat!"

My teeth were clacking so that I could hardly get a word out. "Y-y-yes, sir."

As he kept shaking me the hickory shirt loosened itself and the scrimshaw fell from my waist. It clattered bone-white to the floor. I tried to kick it away, but he was quick to slap his foot on it. He snatched it up and began to chuckle.

"Why, lad, a whale's tooth ain't worth filchin' — didn't you know that?"

"Then why did you come all this way to filch it?" I an-

74

swered, as if it were all a mystery to me and to set his mind at rest.

"Me and Daggatt only want it for sentimental reasons, ye might say. Aye, sentimental reasons."

At last the door flew open and there, gripping a candlestick, stood Mr. Peacock-Hemlock-Jones.

"My dear sir," he snapped. "You must be the noisiest thief in your profession. You will do yourself a service by returning whatever you have found to lay your grubby hands on."

General Scurlock leveled his pistol. "You'll do yourself a service, sir, by standing out of my way."

"Ah. So I see."

He stepped aside to let General Scurlock pass. I was certain Mr. Peacock-Hemlock-Jones would spring into action, and held my breath. But he hardly lifted an eyebrow.

"Do watch your footing on the stairs," he said. "It's dark and you're apt to take a bad spill."

"Aye, I'll be careful," General Scurlock grinned, backing through the door. "The boy'll tell ye I took nothing of worth to ye, so you won't try to follow, now will ye? I can see you've better sense than that."

"You may depend upon it."

"I intend to shy about in the dark and you can expect a pistol ball if you show yourself before morning."

"Good night, sir."

General Scurlock gave a bemused snort, pulled the door closed and was gone. I looked at Mr. Peacock-Hemlock-Jones with a sudden rush of disappointment. He crossed the room and lit the lamp with the flame of his candle. He was smiling.

"We've got to stop him before it's too late, sir!" I said.

"Our visitor, I take it, was your former chimney master, General Scurlock."

"He's got the whale's tooth!"

"That's splendid. I expected him to turn up."

As I gazed at him fresh and awful thoughts started tumbling about in my head. I wondered if I could really trust Mr. Peacock-Hemlock-Jones. He seemed perfectly satisfied that General Scurlock had made off with the treasure map. And now he occupied himself in the mere task of pulling off his boots.

"You want him to get away!" I said.

"Certainly."

My heart began to thump. "You left a trail at every crossroads for him to follow!"

He looked up. "True. I left a trail."

"You're in league with him!"

He returned to his boots. "No. But as long as he has the whale's tooth, Django, we can travel without having to look back over our shoulders. Did you think for a moment you wouldn't be followed?"

"But you admitted you left a trail!" I said.

"A gypsy trail. General Scurlock wouldn't know how to read it."

The rattle of horses' hooves rose from below and I rushed to the window. I got the merest glimpse of the chimney master vanishing phantom-like into the night. And I thought I saw Mrs. Daggatt in the buggy beside him. I turned back to Mr. Peacock-Hemlock-Jones with a desperate, confused feeling. He was chuckling softly.

"The posturing, mutton-headed fool," he said. "Bristling with idle threats."

"But fool enough to make off with the scrimshaw," I said. "And heading straight to Mexico, more'n likely."

"I don't doubt it. But Mexico's a long way off, Django. I expect it'll be a slow race."

"A race?"

He pulled a pin from his waistcoat. "While you slept last night — and you will forgive me, *chavo* — I borrowed the whale's tooth from under your pillow. That engraver staying with us is an exceptional fellow. He did me the service of copying the scrimshaw map on the head of this pin. I'm sure you'll be careful not to lose it."

# 12

## THE MAN WITH THE WHITE GOOSE

The coach was loaded up with food and fodder, and we departed the Red Jacket Inn to the crowing of roosters. It was a fine windy morning, sharp and clear, but the road was still in spring mud.

I urged the horses on as best I could, but I believe snails could have whizzed past us. General Scurlock and Mrs. Daggatt must already be in the next county, I thought.

"No point in hurrying the poor beasts," Mr. Peacock-Hemlock-Jones said, stretching out his legs like a fisherman shipping his oars. "It's more than two thousand miles to Mexico. Plenty of time, Django."

"But General Scurlock's probably streaking along like a cannon shot. He's certain to beat us to Matamoros."

Mr. Peacock-Hemlock-Jones smiled, and then laughed. "Don't count on it, *chavo*. We have a capital advantage. The swaggering imbecile thinks the game's entirely in his own hands. Consider, lad. *You* know it's a race, *I* know it's a race, but *he* doesn't know it's a race. So he's

78

not about to lame his horses by whipping them all the way to the Rio Grande, is he?"

I perked up. Of course! General Scurlock may have darted off with the whale's tooth, but he didn't suspect that I was privy to its secret. Or that Mr. Peacock-Hemlock-Jones had had the treasure map engraved on the head of a pin! That was uncommon smart of him, I thought.

The pin was run through the pocket of my hickory shirt and I kept touching it to make sure it was still there. Mr. Peacock-Hemlock-Jones hadn't been able to buy a magnifying glass. The little fat man had already sold his last one.

"We ought to be able to pick up a glass in Matamoros," Mr. Peacock-Hemlock-Jones said.

"But you said you weren't interested in adventuring after the cactus gold," I remarked.

"I may change my mind," he said, knocking the mud off the soles of his boots with his walking stick. "It will amuse me to pluck the posthole treasure from under General Scurlock's lumpy nose."

"And Mrs. Daggatt, too."

"Especially Mrs. Daggatt," he answered, in jaunty good spirits.

"Then we're going partners?"

"Splendid."

I gave the reins a smart shake, and I'm certain there was a smile on my face. I was sorry I had suspected him the night before of being in league with General Scurlock. He appeared to have forgotten it, and I was grateful. Then

I said, "Won't they be bound to discover we're following along?"

"But we're not."

"I *saw* them, sir."

"You saw them in a buggy. That's hardly a vehicle for a cross-country journey. And Mrs. Daggatt strikes me as a woman who demands every ease and comfort. They fled back to Boston — you can be sure of that."

*Mishto!* Instead of creaking along behind we now appeared to have a fine head start. "Boston, for sure," I agreed. "She gulches down a quantity of food. They'll have to load up an extra wagon."

"I rather imagine she'll attempt to book passage on a ship with a port of call along the Gulf. New Orleans, most likely. They'll be lucky if they don't have to cool their heels in Boston for a month or two."

"Unless General Scurlock comes on alone," I said.

He shook his head. "Those two don't trust each other any further than you can throw a barn, Django. That's obvious, isn't it? They won't allow one another out of each other's sight. Not for an instant."

The thought made me want to laugh. Oh, it was going to be jolly having a partner, and he was owlishly wise. But I did wish the scenery would pass a mite faster. "Are you sure these are racehorses?"

"You have my word for it," he said.

I was glad to see mud time pass. Day by day the roads firmed up and spring came wide-awake. The countryside leafed out, thick and green and new, and you could hear sparrows chasing about through the trees like mice.

As the weeks wore away we covered considerable ground. Mr. Peacock-Hemlock-Jones didn't stop once to ply his trade. I reasoned that he chose to open his paint box only when he ran short of money, and he still had a pocketful.

But he never failed to stretch his legs at every fork and crossroads to mark our journey. We left a gypsy trail from Boston clear to the Mississippi River. By early summer we were joggling through the dust along the river road toward New Orleans.

The nights turned hot as a Dutch oven and we slept out, mostly. Mr. Peacock-Hemlock-Jones was not a man to curl up on the hard ground if he could avoid it. He bought a stout fishnet in Memphis, cut it in two, and we slept in airy hammocks lashed between trees. It was pleasant listening to the bullfrogs croak and the river rush by, but some nights the mosquitoes did make you

81

wish you were somewhere else. They stung everything but the pin in my pocket, and for all I know they bent a stinger or two on that.

I can't say I did much thinking about my pa. It discomposed me some that he might be lurking somewhere along the Mexico border. I'd be glad to snatch up the treasure and make a straight shirttail out of there. I hoped he wouldn't turn up while we were about it. It was enough to chill the spine and I tried to keep my imagination in check.

We stopped in Natchez to have the horses reshod and I remember saying to Mr. Peacock-Hemlock-Jones, "Your cheeks are red as flannel, sir."

"A mere touch of the heat," he scoffed, and we continued on our way.

But the next day, while the sun beat down hot as blazes, he dug out a blanket and wrapped it around himself.

"Are you all right, sir?" I asked.

"Splendid," he said.

But in the middle of the night he had such a chill that the chattering of his teeth woke me. I didn't know what to do for him and began to worry something fierce. By morning I figured we had best turn about for Natchez and find a doctor.

"Natchez?" he scoffed. "Have you lost your reason? You can't win a race by turning around. I'm fit to travel, lad. The sooner we step along the quicker we'll see Matamoros. And not a moment to lose, Django. Shall we be off?"

His teeth had stopped rattling — that was true — but he did appear dreadfully weak climbing onto the coach seat. He wouldn't let me help him. He folded his arms defiantly and we lurched on down the road.

"Wouldn't you like the blanket around you?" I asked.

He dismissed the matter with a scornful smile. "In this heat? Certainly not. Watch that chunk hole in the road, won't you?"

I thought maybe he had thrown off his fever during the night, but by midmorning his teeth began to clack and rattle, and I knew the chills were upon him again. But now he stubbornly refused blankets and forbid me to mention Natchez again.

I drove on. I had never in my life had anyone but myself to care about, and it came as a surprise that every shake of his bones pained me so much. He was in the grip of a high fever. As I rode beside him it was like sitting near a red-hot stove.

His lips looked as dry as bread crusts and before long he stopped making any sense at all. He mumbled and snorted and raged to himself, and I calculated he had slipped out of his mind.

I pulled up on the reins and stopped in the road. I looked behind, over my shoulder. It would use up more than a day to travel back to Natchez, but I made up my mind on the spot and turned the coach around.

"Billygoat! Sunflower!" I cried out. "Step lively, can't you!"

They were strong and steady beasts, but they wouldn't

be rushed. I snapped the reins and thundered at them, but they strolled along like cows.

Not far away I spied a man fishing along the bank of the river.

"Is the nearest doctor in Natchez?" I shouted.

He spit tobacco juice. "Nope," he said.

My heart took a leap. "Where can I find him?"

"You lookin' for a horse doctor or a man doctor?"

"Any doctor'll do," I answered desperately.

"Well, there's Doc Custis. Claims to be a man doctor, but folks around here suspicion he's just a vet with uppity ideas."

"Where is he?"

"You're a-headin' in the wrong direction, son." He pointed south. "Down the road a piece. I saw him not twenty minutes ago. Look for a white house set in a stand of chinaberry trees. If you see a man on the roof with a white goose — that's Doc Custis."

"Thank you, sir."

"Don't thank me, son," he said and returned to his fishing.

I turned the coach about once more and shook the reins. Before long a large white house with four porch columns turned up on the left. It might have been a grand place once, but the paint was peeling off and the yard had shot up in weeds.

Sure enough, a man stood on the roof with a dirty white goose.

# 13

## DR. CUSTIS
## AND OTHER VARMINTS

I pulled into the front yard, scattering hogs and chickens,
and shouted up to the roof.

"You Dr. Custis, sir?"

The man was about to lower the goose down one of the

chimneys on a long rope. He peered at me from under the brim of a floppy straw hat.

"Ain't visitin' hours," he snorted. "Come back next week."

He looked uglier'n homemade soap to me and I wondered if he had all his wits, dropping that honking goose down the chimney.

"This gentleman's dreadful sick," I cried. "A man up the road said you were a doctor."

"Did he? Well, squatters around here are born liars," he grumbled.

"Aren't you Dr. Custis?"

"The doctor is busy. You can see that."

I was desperate. I wished there might be another medical man about, but he would have to do. Mr. Peacock-Hemlock-Jones was now melting away in a heavy sweat.

"This gentleman is mortal sick," I declared. "If you're a doctor you'll surely want to help him."

"He been gun shot?"

"No, sir. Fever and chills and out of his head some."

"Only bilious fever, then. Come back next week at two o'clock."

"No, sir!" I answered stoutly. "He needs tending and I don't aim to move an inch until you come down."

He scowled and pulled out a bandana and wiped his neck. "You better understand I don't accept charity cases."

"We can pay, sir!"

"In what? Pigs and chickens? I got all the livestock I need."

"In cash, sir."

He snorted. "Blast my old shoes if I didn't misjudge you." He hauled up the goose, trussed by its feet and honking and beating its wings, black with soot. "Took you to be squatters. You go on inside and when I'm through sweeping down the chimneys I'll look in on your friend."

I was dumbfounded. "Is that what you're up to with that old goose?"

"Ain't nothin' better'n a live goose to knock down the soot and he don't charge for his services."

"Dr. Custis," I called. "I know chimneys and I'll be proud to scrape your flues clean if you'll hurry on down."

It didn't take him long to make up his mind to that. He appeared to be a sour old pinch-fist, but glad enough to get off that hot roof. He climbed down a ladder and released the goose, which went racing away through the weeds, honking and thrashing its wings.

Up close, Dr. Custis didn't improve any in appearance. He had a short, fat nose, large teeth and eyes sharp enough to skin a fox. His roomy trousers were held up with wide leather braces and as far as I could tell he was still wearing his nightshirt, tucked in.

Together we got Mr. Peacock-Hemlock-Jones in out of the sun and stretched out on a brass bed that was close to falling apart. There were a smart lot of rooms in the house, but not another soul about as far as I could tell.

Mr. Peacock-Hemlock-Jones had sweated through his clothes. He looked as if he had been out in the rain. Dr.

Custis took his pulse, gazing at a heavy turnip watch that I was certain had stopped running. He thumped the chest and raised an eyelid and then announced his medical opinion.

"The man's sick."

"I know that, sir," I said.

"He's feverish."

"Yes, sir."

"And sweatin' like a mule."

"I can see that, sir," I said anxiously. "But what's he got?"

"The ague, if I ain't mistaken."

"You said before it was bilious fever."

"Did I? Well, it's one or the other, that's for certain. Unless it's congestive fever."

I stared at him, full of mistrust and misgiving. "Can't you cipher the difference?"

"It don't hardly matter. The cure's the same — I'll have to leech him."

"Leech him?"

"Draw off the bad blood. My, ain't he weak? He couldn't pull a hen off the roost. Now you trot down the hall to my pharmacy. Second door on the right. You'll find a jar of leeches."

"You sure you can get him well?"

"He'll be fine as silk, and a little finer. Don't worry yourself. Fetch the bloodsuckers."

I took a deep breath and sorely hoped the man knew what he was about. I found the leeches in a large jar of water. They looked like a swarm of yellowish-brown slugs.

When I returned I found Dr. Custis examining the contents of Mr. Peacock-Hemlock-Jones' money pouch. He met my gaze with a snort and a smile. "A man can't be too careful taking in strangers," he said. "I felt it incumbent upon me, you might say, to inventory your gentleman's ability to pay for his keep. I regret to tell you the cure may take two or three weeks."

"You heard me say we had the cash money," I answered, considerably ruffled.

"I do recall, now that you mention it. By heckity, you did indeed."

I set down the jar of leeches and took possession of the money pouch. Dr. Custis was going to bear close attention and I didn't look forward to two or three weeks under the same roof. I wished I had kept going on the road back to Natchez. But when I looked at my friend lying as red as a steamed lobster I knew the trip would have been too much for him.

The doctor dipped his hand into the jar and began applying leeches to Mr. Peacock-Hemlock-Jones' chest. They must have been about an inch long, and once they sank their teeth in they stopped crawling about.

"You sure that's the proper treatment?" I muttered.

"Nothin' improves the health quicker'n the *Hirudo medicinalis*. That's Latin. Ravenous little varmints, ain't they? Look at 'em gorge."

"I'd best water the horses," I said, turning away. I was glad to leave the sickroom. It pained me to see Mr. Peacock-Hemlock-Jones reduced to a state of helplessness, with bloodsucking worms feasting on him.

I unhitched the horses and found a water trough out back. Dr. Custis did know two words of Latin, I told myself, and that was better than none.

I wanted to stay outside. I tied the horses in the shade of a chinaberry tree and stood with them a long while. I was dreadfully afraid for Mr. Peacock-Hemlock-Jones. Leeches or no leeches he might fever up and die. I tried to push the thought out of my head, but tears shot to my eyes. That took me by enormous surprise. I didn't know I cared that much about *anyone*. But Mr. Peacock-Hemlock-Jones was my friend. I took a deep breath and wiped my eyes and tried to watch a flock of birds frolicking about over the river.

After about an hour I returned to the house. The leeches had swelled up as fat as radishes.

Dr. Custis gave a snort of satisfaction. "Looks better already, don't he?"

He didn't look that way to me.

"He's been mumbling all nature of interesting things. Pinheads and postholes." The doctor's eyes began to skin me. "You know anything about that?"

"No, sir," I said quickly. "That's just his name he's trying to tell you."

"His name?"

"Yes, sir." My wits raced along at a howling clip. "Phineas Portroyal."

"Sounded more like pinheads and postholes."

90

"You must have listened wrong," I answered, as innocently as I could. It was fearsome to think that Dr. Custis might discover I was carrying a treasure map engraved on the head of a pin. "His name's Phineas Portroyal."

"Of course, he ain't entirely responsible yet. But I've known men to speak more sense out of their minds than in."

"That's beyond my measure," I answered, and decided I was going to sleep in the same room and try to keep Dr. Custis, with his big ears, at a distance.

He began removing the blood-swollen leeches. "If you plan to take your meals with me," he said, "don't expect anything fancy. I lean to corn bread and common doings."

Common doings, as I was to find out in the days ahead, was ham and bacon. And I found out that Dr. Custis was more interested in bottling his own brand of snake oil medicine than he was in mending the sick. He expected to make a fortune.

I never saw any other patients or servants about the place. I got the feeling that folks in the area would rather see the undertaker than Dr. Custis.

But when he switched from leeches to quinine I must confess that Mr. Peacock-Hemlock-Jones began to improve — to Dr. Custis' surprise, I believe. Still, there were days when the chills and fever returned, and there was nothing to do but worry.

When he was in his right mind I told him that I had changed his name to Phineas Portroyal, which made him laugh. "One day I'll find a name that really suits me," he said.

He apologized for babbling on about pins and treasure holes. But he had lost track of time and when I told him he had been laid up going on two weeks, he fell silent and gloomy.

Then he said, "You jump on Sunflower and beat your way to Matamoros."

I stared at him. "No, sir," I answered. "Partners ought to stick together."

"Don't talk nonsense!" he snapped. "I'm telling you to go. It's precious time lost."

"You're still so precious weak you couldn't pull a hen off the roost," I answered.

In the end he wearied of arguing the matter. Meanwhile, I scraped down all the chimneys with a hoe, being careful to carry the money pouch and the pin in the flues with me. I wasn't about to take any chances with Dr. Custis.

He spent his days tinkering with his bottles and cure-all, and thinking up lies to print on the label. Mr. Peacock-Hemlock-Jones grew stronger every day, it seemed, and by the end of the third week we were able to travel again.

I never hitched up the coach with such uncommon joy. Until Dr. Custis presented his bill.

"I trust you have made an error," said Mr. Peacock-Hemlock-Jones. "Surely your fee is not an outrageous $621!"

"Surely it is, Mr. Portroyal," the doctor replied. "Con-

gestive fever, complicated by the ague, intermittent and
bilious fever."

"You nitwit," snapped Mr. Portroyal. "They're all
the same. It was a common attack of malaria."

"A difference of medical opinion there may be, sir,
but the bill remains $621."

"The fact remains I won't be robbed by a self-educated
quack, sir."

"By heckity! I won't be insulted in my own house, Mr.
Portroyal! I have only to send for the high sheriff and I
shall collect through a court of law."

We could be delayed for months! Then a sudden way

out jolted me like a thunderbolt — and I felt as smart as forty crickets.

"Doctor Custis, sir," I said, in the lofty manner I earnestly admired in Mr. Peacock-Hemlock-Jones. "I think your fee is uncommon reasonable. Indeed I do, sir."

He seemed astonished to find me siding with him, and gave a satisfied snort. But Mr. Peacock-Hemlock-Jones looked at me as if I had lost my reason.

Then I added, "You'll recollect that I scraped down your chimneys. I hope I won't have to call in the high sheriff to collect my fee."

"Your fee?"

"Yes, sir. I calculate it at exactly $621, sir."

Dr. Custis' eyebrows almost shot off his face. He snorted and growled, but there was no further mention of courts of law. I was as entitled to overcharge as he was.

Mr. Peacock-Hemlock-Jones tossed him gold pieces enough to pay for our keep and the use of those pestiferous, gnawing leeches, and we were on our way.

94

# 14

## THE GRASSHOPPER

The whole day long I had the feeling that we were being followed.

I couldn't help glancing back over my shoulder. Finally Mr. Peacock-Hemlock-Jones took the clay pipe out of his mouth. "Expecting someone?"

"Could be the high sheriff after us," I said.

"Mere bluff." And then he broke into a grin. "You whipped that shifty-eyed medicine man at his own game. I'm exceedingly proud of you Django. But for your quick wit we'd be penniless."

I didn't realize how much I had yearned for his approval. I couldn't think what to say, so I kept my eyes on the road ahead and snapped the reins smartly.

"Get along, Billygoat!" I sang out. "You too, Sunflower!"

I awoke in the morning to the scent of woodsmoke in the air and the sizzle of frying fish. When I looked around I thought I must still be asleep. But I wasn't.

I saw a gypsy camp all about us. Three painted wagons

stood unhitched around a morning cook fire. They looked like gingerbread houses on wheels, with curtains at their windows and their front steps pulled down between the shafts. I saw gypsy children climbing through the wild pecan trees for leftover nuts. I saw gypsy women in bright head scarves milking a small herd of goats and men in dark clothes tending their horses.

But I didn't see Mr. Peacock-Hemlock-Jones. And I didn't see his hammock where he'd slung it the night before.

I quickly rolled to my feet. Sunflower was gone. Billy-goat was gone. And the coach was gone.

I froze. I felt discomposed and frightened.

I saw an old blacksmith of a gypsy peering at me. He had great hanging moustaches and a floppy hat tilted to one side of his head. Now that I was awake he seemed to come alive.

*"Dordi! Dordi!"* he exploded with a laugh, revealing several gold teeth. *"Sar shan, chavo? Sar shan?"*

96

I didn't answer. I stared at him, unable to decipher his gypsy lingo.

"How are you, eh? Ah, you have forgotten the *puro jib* — the old language." He pursed his lips, and rings flashed from his fingers as he made a gesture with his hand. "No matter. We will teach you, eh? Come, breakfast is on the fire."

"Where is Mr. Peacock?" I scowled.

"Who?"

"Mr. Hemlock!"

"What?"

"Mr. Jones! My partner!"

"*Avali, avali!*" he laughed again. "Yes, yes, you mean the long-legged one. You mean Chawhoktamengro!"

"Chawhoktamengro?"

"The Grasshopper! His gypsy name, *chavo*. Didn't we pick up his signs out of Natchez, eh? And here we are!" The rings on his fingers flashed again. "But he's gone, Chawhoktamengro is."

"Gone where?"

He shrugged and laughed again. "Come, we will eat."

"I'm not hungry," I answered grimly. Was there no end to the names Mr. Peacock-Hemlock-Jones used on his travels? The Grasshopper! And now he had left me behind among strangers, even if they were gypsies.

I quickly felt for the pin in my pocket. What if he had gone dashing after the treasure for himself? But the pin was still in place.

"Me, I am Tornapo," the old man beamed. "And you are Django, eh? Would you like to see me straighten a horseshoe with my bare hands?"

"I would like you to tell me what has happened," I answered.

"The Grasshopper? What is there to tell? He left."

"But why?" I asked desperately.

"We are gypsies, Django. We don't ask questions."

"You don't answer them, either," I declared sharply.

He laughed, showing me his gold teeth again. "You are safe with us. We will turn you into a fine *romany chal* — a gypsy lad, eh? Come and eat."

By this time others of the tribe had gathered around, gazing curiously at a gypsy who could not speak their *puro jib*. They appeared friendly enough, but I was in no temper to make friends. I felt fiercely wounded. A scaresome thought went streaking through my mind. What if Mr. Peacock-Hemlock-Jones had sold me to these gypsies? I'd heard of such things.

I turned from the pack of them. I'd find out soon

enough where I stood. I untied my hammock and rolled it up tight and slung it over my shoulder.

Tornapo opened his hands in a gesture of deep regret. "You will not even share a meal with us?"

"I'm clearing out," I said.

"But where will you go?"

I glared at him. "I thought you said gypsies didn't ask questions." Then I held my breath and started walking through them. I didn't expect to get very far. They murmured in their *puro jib,* but no one made the slightest move to stop me. By the time I reached the road I was so surprised I almost turned back. They didn't mean to keep me if I didn't want to stay.

"Look for Chawhoktamengro's signs in the road!" Tornapo shouted. *"Avali!* Yes! You will find him."

I turned and gazed at them among the pecan trees. I think I was mortally close to tears. "I won't be looking for him!" I shouted back. I had been buffle-brained to think I had a proper friend in Mr. Peacock-Hemlock-Jones. He had abandoned me in a burnt hurry, like my pa.

Tornapo gave me a sad shrug and a final shout. *"Kushto bak, chavo!* Good luck, boy!"

I turned away and headed south along the river. I would know better than to trust anyone again. Well, I had the pin. I'd go after that posthole treasure myself.

# 15

## THE PIN

I walked all morning long. The road was infernally hot and dusty and I stopped now and again to cool off my feet in the river. I was hungry.

Well, I'd been hungry before. And I'd been on my own before. I calculated I'd make out somehow, but I knew it was a dreadful long way to Mexico.

Of course, I saw the coach's fresh wheel tracks in the dust. At first they riled me, but the longer I walked the less I cared a hoot about Mr. Peacock-Hemlock-Jones. He'd gone his way and I'd go mine, and it would be first rate if our paths never crossed again. First rate and a half. He might at *least* have told me good-bye, I thought, instead of sneaking off like a thief.

I was trying to find some wild berries to eat when I heard goats and saw the gypsy caravan along the road. I had to admit those tall wagons looked grand, carved like palaces and every inch painted blue or green or yellow or red. Even the wheels. I recognized Tornapo driving the first wagon, with a stovepipe sticking up through the roof, and he gave me a wave.

"*Sar shan?*" he called. "How are you, eh?"

I turned away without answering. I wasn't finding any berries, but I pretended I was and after a while the caravan passed me by.

I watched it disappear in its own dust, leaving me behind. I had never felt so desperately alone. I stood there telling myself that I was a gypsy too, even if I couldn't speak the *puro jib,* and I wished Mr. Peacock-Hemlock-Jones *had* sold me to Tornapo and his tribe. At least I'd be sitting in one of those fine carved wagons instead of standing in the dust. And I wouldn't be hungry.

I gave up trying to find berries and plodded on down the road. Maybe I'd come to another stand of wild pecan trees. If I hadn't been so high-headed in the morning I might have at least stuffed my pockets with nuts.

The afternoon wore on, still and hot and buzzing with flies. And then I thought of all the fish in the river and stopped short. Wasn't my hammock fishnet? And wasn't I the greatest muddle-head you ever saw?

I slipped to the water's edge and unrolled the hammock and waded out up to my knees. I gave the net a hurl and watched it settle on the water like a cobweb. It sank slowly and I waited a while, and then hauled it in.

I must have done that a dozen times before I decided there was more to fishing with a net than met the eye. For a moment I considered making a fishhook out of the pin snugged in my pocket. I was hungry enough to try, but not *that* muddle-headed. No, sir!

I threw out the net again and caught a fish.

I could hardly believe my eyes. It flipped and flapped about like a mirror in the sunlight and I wasted no time hauling it in. I caught it under the gills and reckoned I had a three-pounder, at least!

I hurried back up the bank to look for some shade and to build a fire. I was so excited I put together some dry sticks before I realized I had no matches.

I stared at those sticks and I stared at that fish. I would have eaten it raw, but couldn't bring myself to take the first bite.

I rolled up my hammock again, caught the fish under the gills again and started along the road again. I might come to a farmhouse or meet another traveler able to strike fire for me.

But that stretch of road might as well have had a curse on it. I appeared to be the only traveler out in the heat of the day.

There was nothing to do but keep walking. That fish of mine seemed to grow heavier by the mile. The sun was lowering when I thought I heard fiddle music up ahead. I began to run.

The tune grew louder. I was sure now that I would come upon a village or a farmhouse around the bend in the road. But no, sir! I found the gypsy caravan camped in a shimmering thicket of willow trees, and I saw Tornapo sitting on a stump and scraping away on a fiddle.

I stopped short. My pride rose up and I wanted to walk past them. But I couldn't. My stomach felt monstrous empty. I was road weary and dispirited.

I took a deep breath, swallowing my pride, and marched into their camp.

Tornapo lowered his fiddle and the others looked up from their chores.

"*Sar shan?*" I said. "Hello."

Tornapo's face lit up. "What have you got there, *chavo?*"

"A fish. It must be a three-pounder at least. I thought you folks might be hungry."

He wasn't fooled. He laughed, brushing his great moustaches to either side. "Didn't Bibi Mizella — there with the goats — read signs and say a fine three-pound fish would leap into our stewpot, eh? Can anyone *dukker* the future like Aunt Mizella, I ask you? And wasn't I just getting up to make a fire ready?"

"No hurry," I lied.

"But can't you see? Tornapo is hungry!" He got to his feet and called to the old gypsy woman. "Bibi! Fetch us that goat's milk, eh? Sacki! Wild grapes to peck at while this *kushto* fish is cooking. And a few nuts to crack, eh, little Matchka?"

Food came my way from all sides while Tornapo returned to his wagon. It was all I could do to keep from stuffing my mouth. But I held back.

"Eat!" Bibi Mizella said, raising her hands to her hips and looking me over. "I have seen fatter scarecrows."

"Maybe a grape," I answered, plucking one from the bunch.

But it was no use pretending. They knew I hadn't eaten

all day. I stuffed my mouth and finished off a cup of goat's milk. Then they smiled and chattered among themselves and I felt I had been welcomed into the tribe.

Tornapo returned from his wagon with a reading glass, cocked an eye at the sun and set to work.

"You like my *vardo*, eh?" he asked, scraping dry leaves together.

"Your what, sir?" I muttered, crushing a whole mouthful of grapes.

"My wagon." He pointed a finger at a boy with a checked handkerchief tied around his neck. "Sacki, why do you stand there like a stork, eh? Haven't you ever seen a gypsy before? Take Django's fish and clean it, eh?"

Then Tornapo began focusing the sun on the leaves.

Meanwhile, gesturing with his free hand, he began introducing me to his clan, and the air was full of *sar shans*.

"*Sar shan,* Matchka?" I answered. She was about ten years old with two black braids hanging down her back. "*Sar shan,* Artaros? *Sar shan,* Orlenda?" I tried to fix names in my head, but soon lost track.

The pinpoint of sunlight through the glass soon raised smoke among the leaves. Tornapo fanned the spot gently until flames started up and before long he had a cook fire going. He pounded an iron hook into the ground, Bibi Mizella hung a stewpot on it and my fish went into the stew.

It was a grand feast. But by the time everyone sat around the fire I was so full of goat's milk and nuts and wild grapes that I had almost lost interest in the stew.

Everyone praised my fish. It was just what the pot needed, Tornapo insisted. I knew they could get along fine without me, but I was glad to have done a share. I hadn't come into their camp like a beggar.

They had seven horses and Sacki told me the men were all horse traders, and he would grow up to be a horse trader, too.

When the meal was finished Tornapo said, "Listen! Am I not the best fiddler traveling the roads, eh? Django! Go to my *vardo* and bring my fiddle."

I got up. The sun had finally set, but it was a glowing, lingering dusk. I was curious to look inside a gypsy wagon and it wouldn't surprise me if Tornapo had read my mind.

I walked up the steps and opened the half door. I entered a snug room as gaily carved and painted as the outside. There was a wood stove on the left and clothes hanging up and a bunk across the back with the violin propped against the corner.

I started for it when I saw Tornapo's reading glass hanging from a hook on the wall.

I took it down and fingered the pin out of my pocket and bent toward the fading light at a window. I meant to examine my treasure map at last.

I held the glass almost to my eye and brought the pin-head into sharp focus.

It was blank.

# 16

## THE FETCHING STICK

Gypsies clapped hands to Tornapo's fiddle and a woman in a yellow skirt began to dance around the campfire. I sat in the shadows, wrathy and dejected.

I cussed myself for a fool. *There never was a map engraved on the head of the pin*. Mr. Peacock-Hemlock-Jones had lied to me.

He had been up to some devilish mischief all along. It wouldn't surprise me now if he had planned to sniggle that treasure for himself. He might have cut and run for New Orleans, hoping to throw in with Mrs. Daggatt and General Dirty-Face Jim Scurlock. *They* had the whale's tooth. All *I* had to cipher the treasure spot was a worthless pin.

I bent it between my fingers and tossed it away into the leaves.

No wonder he had palmed me off on the gypsies, I told myself. Oh, he was a thumping rogue, with his string of traveling names and his uncommon tricksy ways. I was well shed of him.

After a while I could feel a pair of eyes on me. I looked

up and saw the boy with the bright cloth knotted around his neck. Sacki.

His lips parted in a hesitant smile. He edged closer and finally sat beside me. He was silent a long time. Then he took out a painted stick with stout twine wrapped around it. "You want my *kidda-kosh?*" he asked, offering it to me.

"What?"

"My fetching stick. Watch." He unwrapped the twine and then flicked it toward an empty berry basket standing a few feet away. The blob of lead at the tip of the twine whipped itself around the handle and he jerked the basket to our feet.

"I have caught rabbits with my *kidda-kosh,*" he said. "My old granddad taught me how. You want to try it?"

It looked easy enough. But I whipped that *kidda-kosh* again and again without fetching anything. He never once laughed at me.

"It takes practice," he said solemnly.

I nodded and offered it back.

But he threw up his hands and smiled again. "No. From me, Sacki."

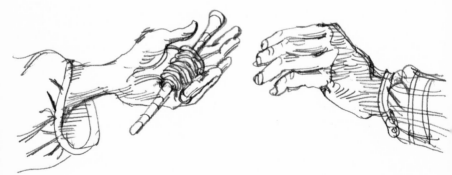

"You'll need it yourself, more'n likely," I said.

"I can make myself another one. Keep it."

I looked at the stick, carved and painted bright gypsy colors like the wagons. I could tell he valued it. But finally I cleared my throat and told him I was obliged.

His smile widened. "You like it here with us?"

I gazed at the gypsies clapping to the fiddle and at the high wagons reflecting the firelight. I nodded.

"You want Bibi Mizella to fix a ring in your ear?"

"No," I answered.

"It doesn't hurt."

"I don't fancy myself with a ring in my ear."

"But you are a *romany*. A gypsy. Tornapo said so. See, I have a fine gold ring in my ear. Doesn't it shine even here in the dark?"

I didn't say anything. I remembered the large gold rings dangling from my mother's ears.

"Ah, you miss your friend," he said. "I am sorry."

"He's not my friend," I answered sharply, and flicked out the *kidda-kosh*.

He nodded with quick understanding. "Tornapo says he's a *gorgio*."

I stared at him. "What's a *gorgio*?"

"An outsider. No gypsy blood. A *gorgio* cannot be trusted. All the traveling people know that." Then he took the fetching stick from my hand and picked up a fallen twig off the ground, to show me again how it was done.

Suddenly, as if I had been struck deaf, there wasn't a sound around the gypsy fire. Tornapo's fiddle stopped short, clapping hands froze in midair and the dancers began fading back into the shadows.

Three creatures loomed up, glowering at us, with muskets cradled in their arms.

They were great, hairy men, and in the firelight their round faces glowed like pumpkins.

Finally, one of them spoke up, after they all took a moment to spit tobacco juice.

"Any of you chicken thieves talk English?"

Tornapo got to his feet, and he was as big as any of them. "We are not chicken thieves, sir gentlemen."

"You're gypsy-people ain't you?"

"Yes."

"Then you're chicken thieves." He spit again. "Clear out."

I thought certain we were in for a fight. Didn't Tornapo say that he could straighten a horseshoe with his bare hands? But he only smiled as if they were making polite conversation. "Now, sir gentlemen, you can see that we are not bothering anyone."

"You're a-botherin' us."

"But even birds of passage must stop to rest."

"Not in our neck of the woods, you ain't," the man said. "Ain't none of you foreigners goin' to neighbor up to us. Now git!"

I was surprised to see that the gypsies had already begun to hitch up their wagons. It appeared nothing uncommon for them to be ordered to move on. But it was uncommon to me, and my blood began to simmer. Even Sacki was gone from my side, busy in the shadows of his wagon.

"As you wish," Tornapo said, unruffled. "As you wish, sir gentlemen."

It didn't take five minutes before the wagons and the goats and the horses were moving out. I felt riled, but powerless. Then Tornapo came by, driving his *vardo,* and yanked me up by the arm to the seat beside him.

"Keep silent, *chavo,*" he whispered.

"But they had no right!" I protested.

He shrugged.

I looked at his bare, blacksmith's arms and felt sorely disappointed in him. "You could have knocked their heads together, couldn't you?"

111

"*Avali*. Yes. And sent them running with their muskets wrapped around their necks. But why bother? We don't fight over a patch of ground. We leave that to the *gorgies*. The world is wide, eh, Django? There is always another patch of ground."

I could hear the three men laughing at us. Finally I said, "I'll never trust a *gorgio* again."

Tornapo looked at me and didn't seem pleased by my remark. "Listen to me, *chavo*. Some *gorgies* are worse than others. Some are better. Don't put them into the same pot."

We reached the road and I fell silent. It appeared to me that gypsies were not much different from orphans. No one really wanted them about, and they had to make their way as best they could.

For the first time I began to feel like a gypsy through and through. I didn't want a ring in my ear, but I did admire the bright silken cloths Sacki and Tornapo and the other men wore about their necks.

"Ah, you mean a *diklo*," Tornapo said. "Look inside the wagon. Behind the door. Choose any color you want. It doesn't matter. I have only green ones."

I returned with a green *diklo* knotted around my neck, and Tornapo nodded. "Don't you look like a real *romanychal* now, eh, Django?" I nodded and he laughed. "You would like to travel the roads with us? You have other plans?"

"No," I muttered.

"*Mishto!*" he said. "Then it is settled."

112

I had already noticed that we had turned north up the road, back toward Natchez. Well, it didn't matter to me. One direction was as good as another.

But we hadn't gone more than a mile when Tornapo halted the caravan. He ordered it about and we retraced our steps.

We were soon camped again. Under the same willow trees we had left an hour before. "Will those sir gentlemen think to find us here?" Tornapo laughed quietly. *"Kek! No!"*

I looked about and smiled. Tornapo had his pride and meant to camp where he pleased. And those sir gentlemen be hanged!

# 17

## THE HORSE TRADE

Dawn was hardly aglow through the trees when we took to the road again and headed south. I sat on the wagon beside Tornapo and practiced whipping out the *kidda-kosh*. I aimed at everything loose beside the road, and once succeeded in fetching a broken gourd.

"Bravo!" Tornapo roared.

"I reckon I'm getting the hang of it," I said.

Then my eye caught a freshly broken willow stick poked in the ground. I was about to try for it when I stopped short. I recognized it for what it was — one of Mr. Pea-cock-Hemlock-Jones's markers.

I'm sure Tornapo saw it, too, but you'd never guess from his face.

He said nothing and we passed on.

Finally I asked, "Don't you leave signs behind you like — like the Grasshopper?"

"Signs? Ah, you mean a *patrin*. Yes. Artaros, following with the goats, he is leaving our *patrin*."

"But why?"

"It is a way gypsies have of finding each other, eh? Yes,

I must teach you to read our *patrin*. Then you will always be able to find us."

I looked at him. "Do you mean you can tell exactly whose *patrin* it is?"

"As if his name was nailed to the road!" Tornapo laughed.

"Then you knew it was the Grasshopper's *patrin* you found outside Natchez?"

"Of course, *chavo*. And that he was not traveling alone, as he is now."

"But how?"

He seemed pleased to be initiating me into gypsy secrets. "He cut his sticks with the short stub of a branch left on, eh? That was you, that stub!" And the morning sun glinted off his gold teeth as he laughed again.

"But he's a *gorgio*," I said with rising anger, as if he had no right to a gypsy *patrin*.

"True. But Chawhoktamengro has traveled the roads with gypsies. He has learned our ways."

I looked hard at Tornapo. "Did you know my pa, sir?"

He didn't face me. "Doesn't one gypsy know another?" he shrugged.

"Was there bad blood between him and the Grasshopper?"

"It is possible. Look there! Isn't that a fine city up ahead, eh? Maybe we will trade a horse or two."

It wasn't a city at all. It was only a dusty village with a rickety steamboat landing and a sawmill and a smelly tanning yard that made you want to pinch your nose. I'm not certain Tornapo really planned to stop there at all, but as we passed along the shady street I was quick to notice the cut stick poking out of some weeds. It was Mr. Peacock-Hemlock-Jones's *patrin*, all right, and I saw that there was no branch stub left on.

Well, he had shed himself of me — I could read that for myself. But I also noticed fresh tufts of grass thrown between the ruts of the street. I calculated Tornapo read more into *that* than I could, for he began to nod to himself. Then he said, "Yes. A fine place to trade horses."

We camped on the outskirts of the village. No one seemed in a great hurry. Bibi Mizella began milking the goats. Sacki's little sister, Matchka, had her black hair freshly braided and set off with her mother in their brightest skirts to read fortunes. The men discussed which horses to trade. Sacki wanted to go along, but Bibi Mizella rattled off some *puro jib* in his direction and he gave out a deep sigh.

"Aunty says you and me's got to peddle the milk," he grumbled. "We'll never learn horse tradin' that way."

"I wish I knew how to read fortunes," I said.

"Aw, that's women's work," he glowered. "Horses are men's work. No one knows more about horses than us gypsies."

Finally we set out with pails of goats' milk. Tornapo stayed behind to shoe one of the wagon horses.

We knocked at back doors. But I noticed that Sacki was careful to avoid certain houses.

116

"What's wrong with that one?" I asked, pointing to a white frame home behind a swaybacked picket fence.

"It has the mark on it."

"What mark?"

He pointed out a scratch in the gatepost:

‡

"Gypsies have been here before us," he said. "That means to avoid this place. They'll set their dogs on us."

We moved on to another house and Sacki's eyes picked out a circle and a dot carved in an old shade tree.

⊙

"Good," he nodded. "Here they are friendly to us."

It was true. The lady bought a pitcher of goats' milk and offered us some freshly baked cookies.

It was astonishing the things Sacki could tell me about the people in the village as we wandered about.

"An old woman died in that house not long ago," he said, pointing to the *patrin*.

"And here they are stingy people, wouldn't give you a drink of water."

✝

"Ah, there is a good house," he continued. "The fine mistress likes to have her fortune told. See?"

Δ

"And she wants a baby. See, again?"

〜〜〜
〜〜〜

"But what good is it to know all that?" I asked.

He laughed. "It is for *dukkering*. The fortune-telling. My mam and little Matchka will read the marks outside the house and surprise the fine mistress with what they see in the lines of her hand. 'Ah, fine mistress,' they will say. 'You have no children and it makes you sad. You wish a baby. Yes, a fine baby would make you happy, fine mistress.' Oh, they will spin things out and *dukker* a good future and the fine mistress will feel happy."

It must have taken us an hour to sell the goats' milk. Then, with money in our pockets, we strolled along the village street, gazing into the barbershop and pressing our noses against the windows of the general store. But the money wasn't ours to spend.

We continued on toward the sawmill and I felt as much a gypsy as Sacki, with the *diklo* knotted to one side of my neck and my eyes peeled for secret signs.

We were moving past a high fence along the tannery when we discovered we were no longer alone. There must have been five or six village boys following in our tracks, and they didn't look overly friendly. The tallest of them had a neck that stuck up like a turkey's, and he did the talking.

"Howdy," he grinned.

"Howdy," I answered.

"What you been sellin'?"

"Goats' milk," Sacki answered. He could feel trouble in the air and so could I. But there was nothing to do but stand our ground.

"You got a legal license to sell goats' milk?"

"No," I said. There was going to be a fight no matter what we answered, so I added, "You got a legal license to ask hairbrained questions?"

His grin widened while he searched his head for an answer. I decided he wasn't as smart as he should have been. I began looking about for some way out of this mischief.

"You oughten to bad-mouth me," he said finally.

"Only trying to make polite conversation," I said.

"Well, polite ain't good enough. Reckon we'll have to impound your goat money."

"We spent it," I said. "Every last cent, at the general store. You run over there and tell them we said you could impound it."

His face got tired of holding the grin. "Reckon we got no choice but to whip you."

Out of the corner of my eye I saw Sacki's hand edge toward his pocket. I hoped he didn't have a knife in there. His face was dark and brooding, and I was certain he had been in scrapes like this more than once. *"Kek,"* I muttered under my breath. *No.*

His eyes flashed my way. He must have thought I had lost my wits. But if I had learned anything from Mr. Peacock-Hemlock-Jones it was to use my head, and quick as possible.

"Agreed," I declared. "Whip us, but whatever you do, don't throw us over this fence."

"What?"

I glanced fearsomely at the high fence, posted with KEEP OUT signs. "Break our bones. Bloody our noses. But please, whatever you do — *don't throw us over that scaresome tall fence!*"

I saw his eyes light up. His friends closed in on us like a pack of wolves.

"This'll learn you not to bad-mouth me!"

And over the fence we went. We landed in the tannery yard, looked at each other, jumped up like fleas and ran.

Of course they came howling after us. But we had a

thumping head start. They stopped short of the camp when they saw Tornapo and the other men, who had returned from their horse trading.

They pitched a few stones, but when Tornapo raised himself to his full height they decided it was a risky pasttime and ran.

Once we caught our breath Sacki began to laugh so hard they must have been able to hear it in the village. The air filled with the *puro jib,* and soon everyone was laughing but me.

I was gazing at two horses the gypsy traders had brought back to camp.

They were Billygoat and Sunflower.

# 18

## THE MAN IN THE RAIN

Tornapo came over to me and said, "You know those horses, eh? You think we made a good trade?"

I knew that Mr. Peacock-Hemlock-Jones valued his coach horses above most things, and I might have leaped to the conclusion that some misfortune had befallen him. But I didn't. I wasn't fooled. He had left the animals behind for Tornapo to gather up. Even I could read his *patrin,* and I was certain the tufts of grass had led the gypsy horse traders directly to Billygoat and Sunflower.

"It's none of my affair," I answered solemnly. The truth was I felt a secret joyfulness at the sight of those great, easy-tempered horses. We had come a thousand miles together and they seemed the nearest thing to old friends I had. "But you forgot to trade back for the coach," I added.

"The coach?" He laughed and tugged at his hat. "The coach is not here. Our friend only changed horses. Fresh horses. Oh, he was in a big hurry, wasn't he, eh?"

In a big hurry to join up with Mrs. Daggatt and General Dirty-Face Jim Scurlock, I thought. "Your friend," I murmured scornfully. "Not mine."

He spread his hands in an open gesture. "Why do you say that? He has not harmed you, *chavo.*"

I almost explained how he had humbugged me with the treasure map and the pin. But I shrugged instead, and walked off to sit by myself. There seemed no escaping Mr. Peacock-Hemlock-Jones. I could feel his presence like a cunning spirit lurking about the camp. He had flummoxed Tornapo as easily as he had me, and I calculated he'd turn up when he was ready to claim his horses.

Day by day we followed the river, selling goats' milk and horse-trading, but mostly living off the land. New Orleans couldn't be much further off. Sacki trapped a porcupine and brought it into camp like a great trophy.

"A *hatchi-witchu!*" Bibi Mizella exclaimed, and I gave a start. I recalled that word from long ago, even if I had forgotten what it meant. It was a grand word — I used to run the sound of it over my tongue — and I was sorely disappointed that it was only *puro jib* for a pesky porcupine.

"The gypsies clustered around and Tornapo grinned. "Have you ever seen such a fine, fat one, eh!"

I turned to Sacki. "What's it good for?"

"Good?" He seemed amazed at my simplemindedness. "Have you never eaten a *hatchi-witchu?* There's nothing better! We'll have a feast tonight!"

Bibi Mizella took charge. She stuffed it with nuts and wild garlic and wrapped it with a thick layer of river mud. Then she buried it in the hot ashes to bake.

123

I didn't intend to be that hungry for supper. But as night fell and we sat around the campfire I decided that if I was going to live with gypsies I had best learn to eat porcupine.

And I did have a taste. Bibi Mizella cracked open the mud ball and I was surprised to see that the quills and skin came away with it, leaving the steaming, garlicky treat. Tornapo carved it up and offered pieces all around. I accepted a chunk and after a while ventured to take a nibble. I must confess it was tender and juicy, but I was glad there wasn't enough for second helpings. Porcupine was porcupine and it would take some getting used to.

"Good, yes?" Sacki asked, licking his fingers.

I grinned and nodded. "First rate," I said. "First rate and a half. That's the best *hatchi-witchu* I ever ate."

Soon Tornapo began scraping away on his fiddle and there was the usual dancing and hand-clapping around the campfire. Sacki climbed a tree and said he could see the lights of New Orleans downriver, but no one seemed to care.

I sat practicing with my fetching stick and told myself that Mr. Peacock-Hemlock-Jones had done me a service running out on me. Was there a jollier life than traveling the roads in a gypsy wagon? I might grow up to be a horse trader, like Sacki, and have a fine painted *vardo* of my own.

Tornapo must have fiddled away for two hours straight. But finally he called a halt and went to bed. I stretched my hammock between two trees and curled up for the night.

I could hear a distant rumble of thunder and the sky darkened over with clouds.

I don't know how long I had been asleep when the clouds burst open and a warm, spattering downpour woke me. When I opened my eyes I saw a light burning in Tornapo's wagon and then I saw a man approaching through the rain. He stopped and looked at me, with the cloudburst pouring off the brim of his hat.

"*Sar shan,* Django?"

It was Mr. Peacock-Hemlock-Jones.

I didn't move. I only stared at him. Drops of rain blurred my eyes. Then I curled up tighter and turned my back to him.

"Come, come," he said. "Did you think I wouldn't be back for you? I'm surprised at you, *chavo.*"

I didn't answer.

"You'll drown in that fishnet," he said. "Do get up."

"Leave me alone," I muttered.

"I've come to fetch you."

I turned my head and peered at him standing in the rain and grinning like the Devil himself. "Fetch your horses," I said. "I aim to stay here."

It was a moment before he answered. "You like being a gypsy, I see. Splendid. But there'll be time for that later. We've treasure to run for, and there's not a moment to lose."

I shot another glance at him. "Don't think you can

fingle-fangle me again!" I declared. I almost had to shout through the roar of the cloudburst. "There was no map on the head of that pin you gave me. Nothing! I looked."

"Correct. But didn't it keep your hopes alive all these long weeks on the road? Admit it."

"We have no map. I expect you've thrown in with Mrs. Daggatt and General Scurlock."

"What a preposterous notion! But I don't intend to stand out here in the rain all night discussing the matter. Shake yourself out of that hammock and let's be on our way. I have a boat waiting."

This news gave me a proper start. A boat! The very word set my thoughts jumping. But then I reminded myself that he was most likely humbugging me again.

"You didn't so much as say good-bye when you ran off," I declared. "You're no better'n my own pa, and a whole lot worse!"

"I did say good-bye. I just didn't want to wake you."

*"But why?"*

The rain kept sloshing down off his hat. "After the weeks lost with that fool doctor I was in a decided hurry to reach New Orleans. I drove day and night, trading off for fresh horses. You would have wanted to come along. Now, that's the truth, isn't it, Django?"

"But I wouldn't have been in your way," I said.

"What if they had caught sight of you?"

"Who?"

"Mrs. Daggatt and General Scurlock. I meant to learn

126

whether they had landed in New Orleans, as I suspected."

I sat up. "Did they?"

"They did. One glimpse of you would have put them on guard. They knew you had had a chance to examine the whale's tooth. One glimpse of me and I'd have insisted you had run off long ago. And it almost came to that. I caught sight of them along the wharves trying to book passage to Mexico. But they didn't lay eyes on me. I'm sure of that."

Despite myself I said, "Then they've got the jump on us!"

"They left yesterday morning. By wagon and a string of packhorses. I strongly suggest you stir yourself!"

I hesitated. But then I got to my feet and began rolling up the hammock. "Why didn't they take a ship, too?"

"They couldn't find one. There's not a chip of wood sailing to Matamoros for the next three months."

"But you said there's a boat waiting for us."

"Indeed there is. I expect to make good time on the water."

"But how did you book pasasge?"

"I didn't. I bought the boat."

# 19

## THE RIVER SWAN

The boat was so old and weathered it looked like drift-wood timbers someone had pegged together. It was broad and snub-nosed and seemed dreadful small to make a sea voyage in. There was a crooked pole that served as a mast,

128

with traces of the bark still on it. The cabin was hardly worth mentioning. In the lantern light I made out a pot-bellied stove, a rail around the stern and what I took to be a cargo of wet sawdust leaking out from under a heavy canvas.

"Welcome aboard the *River Swan*," said Mr. Peacock-Hemlock-Jones. "Let's cast off."

We had ridden Billygoat and Sunflower bareback through the downpour, which had now slacked off. Mr. Peacock-Hemlock-Jones indicated a kind of corral he had had built forward of the mast. We penned the horses and I helped pull in the mooring lines. We began floating with the current and he stationed himself at the tiller.

"Hadn't we better raise the sail?" I asked.

"If you wish," he answered.

I had spent hours on end watching the ships in Boston Harbor and thought I had some notion of how things were done. "Sure you know how to sail a boat?" I said.

"I haven't the faintest idea," he answered. "But it can't be very difficult. The former owner — a Captain Cyprian — was a gentleman of the most impressive ignorance. We'll get the hang of things."

The sail was thin as a bed sheet and I managed to get it raised.

Fortunately, at that dark hour of the night, we had the river to ourselves and weren't likely to run into anything.

I watched the lights of New Orleans drift by. Then I said, "What's all that sawdust for?"

"To keep the ice from melting."

"What ice?"

"Under the sawdust. The *River Swan* is an ice scow. Captain Cyprian was in the trade of cutting ice in the snowfields up north and selling it during the summer in New Orleans. Unfortunately a couple of rats were discovered frozen in his product, and he has been unable to give away his cargo. He jumped at the chance to sell out."

I learned that Mr. Peacock-Hemlock-Jones had scurried about the city painting portraits to raise money, and had had to sell his coach as well. He had stocked the boat with oats and provisions. He hadn't sold the horses, but traded them back to Tornapo for Billygoat and Sunflower.

"It leaves us quite bankrupt ourselves," he admitted, lighting his clay pipe. "Of course, we might be able to sell the ice in Matamoros. It's apt to prove quite a novelty in those hot latitudes. But I don't mind admitting I've gambled everything on your treasure."

I flashed him a cautious look. I was no longer certain what to believe or how I felt about him. "We have no map," I said. "You know that full well."

He pushed hard on the tiller. "I know nothing of the sort. You're forgetting I'm known in some quarters as Charles Balthazar Jones, *artiste extraordinaire*."

"You travel under so many names I don't know who you are," I murmured.

"Sometimes I forget myself," he grinned. "But you can be certain of one thing. I've an artist's eye. That map's etched in my head. I could sketch it with my eyes shut."

When dawn broke we were afloat in the Gulf of Mexico.

He knew no more about navigation than I did, but the problem didn't trouble him for a moment. He turned the tiller over to me and told me to keep the shoreline in view on our right. That way it would be impossible to get lost.

"Has it occurred to you, sir, that we're taking a riverboat into the open sea?" I remarked.

"Water is water," he answered, dismissing the matter with a wave of the hand.

"Don't you calculate she's flat-bottomed, being a river scow?"

"I haven't the slightest notion," he replied. "And I don't intend to look."

Fortunately the sea was calm and I must admit it was almighty pleasant sailing along through the soft morning air. Gulls wheeled about to have a look at us from time to time, and what they thought at the sight of two horses at sea, munching oats, I couldn't imagine.

Mr. Peacock-Hemlock-Jones busied himself at the old wood stove, cooking up a skillet of fresh shrimp. He had spared no expense, it appeared to me, in provisioning the boat. He opened a tin of peaches and we ate breakfast under the canvas awning hanging in shreds over the tiller.

The day passed like a dream and I didn't care if I never set foot on dry land again. I kept the thin shoreline on our right, and we lumbered along free as a fish. There were moments when it struck me as foolhardy to be sailing with a boat captain who clearly had never been to sea before, but the thought didn't appear to trouble him.

We took turns at the tiller and it didn't take me long

to explore every inch of the *River Swan*. The sawdust covering the huge ice block must have been three feet thick to keep it from melting. I dug down and discovered enough shrimp and lobster on ice to last for weeks to come, and a brace of pheasants as well. Mr. Peacock-Hemlock-Jones was certainly a man to travel in comfort.

"I don't see any frozen rats," I said.

"Then help yourself."

I chipped off a piece of ice to suck on, the day having warmed up considerably, and joined him in the shade of the awning. He sat with an arm around the heavy tiller and his feet propped on an overturned bucket.

"I don't see an anchor anywhere aboard," I said.

"We won't be needing one," he answered.

I stared at him. "You aim to sail at night, sir?"

"That's my intention. It's the only way to make up for lost time."

I suddenly wished I knew how to swim. Then it occurred to me that if we ran aground in the night I'd only get my feet wet. I'd be able to walk ashore.

I sucked on the chunk of ice. "Was it the gypsies who told you about my pa?" I asked suddenly.

"Told me what?"

"That's he's likely somewhere along the Mexican border."

"We'll find him," he answered, puffing away at his pipe.

"I'm not looking for him," I muttered. "You are, sir."

"That's clearly understood," he said.

"What do you aim to do if you catch up with him?"

He pulled down the brim of his hat. He peered at the distant horizon. But he didn't answer.

We had all day to get the hang of tacking about in the wind and managed not to run aground that night. Not that there was any moon to light the shore. But when we ventured too close we could hear the hiss of the surf. Then we got busy and steered away.

The weather held steady as you could please. There was a smart little breeze, enough to swell the sail. When I had nothing better to do I set up a piece of stove wood and practiced with my fetching stick. I was getting so I hardly missed.

Within a week I came to feel like an able-bodied seaman. I was taking a strong fancy to the *River Swan*. She might be slow and flat-bottomed and not much to look at, but she was a friendly old scow. And hard-working as a mule.

With the treasure money, I thought, we might build a new cabin and paint her up in bright colors, like a gypsy *vardo,* and have a fine boat to adventure in.

But I suspicioned that Mr. Peacock-Hemlock-Jones was already making plans of his own, and I calculated they didn't include me. He was a lone kind of man. The day would come when he'd decide we ought to go our separate ways. Well, maybe I'd buy the *River Swan* with my share of the treasure.

Several days later we spotted wild cattle strung along the surf and cooling off in the breakers.

"Longhorns," Mr. Peacock-Hemlock-Jones remarked.

I watched them for hours. "How far do you reckon we've come?"

"We're making splendid time. Splendid. It wouldn't surprise me if we run smack into Mexico any day now. Mrs. Daggatt and the General are certainly trailing behind."

I fed the horses and drew buckets of seawater to wet down the sawdust. The day was heating up something fierce. The ice was a valuable cargo and it wouldn't do to reach Matamoros without the price of a shovel.

Toward noon the breeze died away. The sail fell slack as a curtain.

I said, "We've lost the wind."

"Nothing to worry about, *chavo*. It'll spring up again."

We sat becalmed for six confounded days.

# 20

## THE CAKE OF ICE

A breeze sprang up in the night. Only it wasn't a breeze. It was a howling wind.

I was awakened as the *River Swan* gave a sudden lurch. Then her flat bottom smacked the water like a cannon shot, and we were off among the swells.

I was on my feet by then and so was Mr. Peacock-Hemlock-Jones. "Grab the tiller!" he cried out, making for the mast. "We'll head her in to shore!"

Again the boat cracked against a swell and threw us off our feet. She bucked and rolled and groaned in all her joints. I crawled to the stern on my hands and knees, with water exploding from the bow. When I reached the tiller it was whipping about something fearful. I finally caught hold, but not for long. The boat gave another lurch and the tiller almost heaved me overboard.

I returned to the battle. The scow dipped and rose and slammed against the sea. I caught sight of Mr. Peacock-Hemlock-Jones amidship trying to take in the sail before we capsized. But the next thing I knew the mast snapped and the canvas flew off like a newspaper in the wind.

The night was infernally dark. I could hear the whinnying of the horses in their corral.

Finally Mr. Peacock-Hemlock-Jones joined me at the stern and together we got the tiller more or less tamed. I'd have been glad to head for shore, but we were so turned around I wasn't sure where it stood. Neither was he.

"Maybe we ought to head into the wind!" I shouted. "I've always heard that!"

"Capital!" he answered. "A splendid idea!"

But we couldn't head into the wind. With the sail gone the boat wouldn't respond to the tiller.

"I believe this calls for a sea anchor," Mr. Peacock-Hemlock-Jones remarked, and I realized with a start that he knew more about boats than he had let on. "Quickly. Come on."

Together we loosened the iron, potbellied stove and shifted it forward. Then he loosened the tarpaulin lashed down over the ice and we rolled the stove onto the canvas. He drew up the corners, forming a weighted sack, and secured it to the stout forward towline.

"Over the side, *chavo!*" he shouted.

We lifted the sea anchor and dropped it over the bow. It sank like a stone, stretching the rope tight, and the boat began swinging around into the wind.

"Perfect," he said. "Excellent. We should ride out the weather nicely."

All night long the boat jerked about like a wild animal on a tether. The flat bottom slapped against the sea and nearly jarred my teeth loose. I was certain we would burst into kindling any moment.

But we didn't. The *River Swan* was sturdy as an ox. Somehow we got through the night, and in the hours before dawn the winds eased to a mere whistle and the sea got tired of heaving about. It flattened out as the storm whisked itself away, leaving behind a scattering of whitecaps like tufts of cotton.

The day broke clear and still, as if to mock the roaring hours of the night. It was no surprise that the shoreline had disappeared from view. We had drifted far to sea.

The boat was ankle-deep in water. She was loose in all her joints and couldn't last much longer. But we were still afloat, and that was enough for Mr. Peacock-Hemlock-Jones.

We set about the task of hauling up the canvas sea anchor. Then he knocked apart the corral for its timbers, giving the horses the freedom of the boat, and managed to lash together a short mast. Together we rigged up something of a sail with the wet canvas and he cocked an eye toward the sun. Then he pointed west.

"If Mexico's not in that direction somebody moved it," he smiled, and took the tiller. The *River Swan* began inching westward.

I fetched a bucket and began to bail out the boat. But the more I bailed the more I suspicioned the worst. "I think we're springing one leak after the other," I said.

"No doubt," he answered, undaunted, and lashed the

tiller in place. We both busied ourselves with buckets.

By noon it seemed to me that we had bailed out half the Gulf of Mexico, but we were still ankle-deep in water.

When the shoreline appeared like a streak of white chalk on the horizon I gave a leap and a yell and thought we were saved. Never did I see such a welcome sight.

"Keep bailing," Mr. Peacock-Hemlock-Jones said, without bothering to look up.

Hour by hour the shore drew closer and the water about our feet grew deeper. We couldn't have been more than a mile from land when the tired old bottom timbers gave up the ghost. Seawater gushed in and the *River Swan* gave a final groan and sank from under our feet.

It happened so fast I didn't have time to grab out for something to hold onto. Billygoat and Sunflower were in the sea around me and so was Mr. Peacock-Hemlock-Jones.

"Catch one of the horses by the mane!" he yelled. "Or the tail!"

But for the first moment I was so occupied trying to keep my head above water that all I could do was kick and thrash. By the second moment the horses were already out of reach and swimming in a panic toward shore.

Mr. Peacock-Hemlock-Jones grabbed me by the shirt collar. "Where in tarnation did you learn to swim *that* way?" he said.

"I'm not swimming," I sputtered. "I'm drowning."

"Nonsense."

Only a few chunks of stove wood were left of the *River*

138

*Swan.* But the huge cake of ice had floated free and bobbed about as slick as glass.

He dragged me toward it. Less than a foot rose above the surface, but for me it was like touching land. It was smooth and slippery and I had a terrible time climbing aboard. He finally gave me a mighty heave and there I was — flat on a block of ice.

We could hear the distant crack of surf along the beach, and after a while he determined that the tide was rushing in.

"There's not room for the two of us up there," he said. "You'll float ashore."

"Yes, sir," I muttered. "Don't worry about me. I'll be fine."

I held his wrist a long time while he rested himself in

the water. It seemed like the first time I had actually touched him. A moment later he was gone, swimming toward the beach.

I calculated I hadn't a thing to worry about as long as I held on. Of course, the ice was freezing one side of me and the sun was baking the other. But I *was* drifting closer to shore.

I would have been glad to thaw one side of me and freeze the other, but every time I tried to turn over on the glassy surface I felt myself slip. So I just held on.

It was a while before I awoke to the fact that the ice was melting away in the tropic waters. The sun wasn't helping any either.

Directly I was lying more in the water than out. The cake of ice was shrinking fast. Earlier I hadn't had time to realize that I was scared, but now I had plenty of time. I was scared. By the time I reached the breakers I was hanging onto a puny lump of ice. I wanted to call out to Mr. Peacock-Hemlock-Jones, but when I raised my head he was gone from the beach.

A wave caught me and tore me loose from the ice. I was certain I was a goner, and went tumbling underwater. A moment later I was astonished to be able to rise on my feet.

I was standing in shallow water.

I shook myself off and walked ashore, feeling silly as a goose. Mr. Peacock-Hemlock-Jones reappeared on the crest of a sand dune. He had gone to fetch up the horses.

We sat in the warm sand for a while and took stock.

Our provisions were gone and we hadn't a drop of fresh water to drink. We didn't exactly know where we were or if there was a town within fifty miles. But we had horses to ride and, amazingly, I still had the fetching stick in my back pocket.

"Are you rested?" Mr. Peacock-Hemlock-Jones asked.

"Yes, sir."

"No point in sitting here. Let's go."

We started along the beach bareback. I glanced over the water, but Mr. Peacock-Hemlock-Jones's fortune in ice had melted away to the small end of nothing.

# 21

## THE MARK OF A THIEF

Mr. Peacock-Hemlock-Jones hadn't the slightest notion of perishing for lack of food or water. We rode bareback and along the way picked cactus apples, which were juicy and sweet, although infernally shot through with hard little seeds.

The next morning we stumbled into a small fishing village, and discovered we were in Mexico. But we had overshot Matamoros.

There were only three families in the village and Mr. Peacock-Hemlock-Jones chattered away in their own lingo. They wouldn't let us go without feasting us as best they could. Then he found a lump of charcoal and nothing would do but what every family pose for him, children and all. There wasn't a scrap of paper to be found in the village, but that didn't stop him. He drew a family portrait on a plaster wall inside each house. It wouldn't surprise me if they were still there.

Before we left they loaded us up with a goatskin of fresh water, straw hats, a string of dried fish and corn for the horses. We waved at each other like old friends and started north.

"The way you rattled off their talk is something amazing," I said.

"We'll be crossing a stream or two," he replied thoughtfully. "They warned us to watch out for quicksand."

We were two days reaching Matamoros.

The town sprawled upriver along the Rio Grande, baking in the sun. I was never so happy to see a place in my life. Dusty palm trees shot up along the riverbank and cotton stretched out behind the town like a field of snow.

I could see an old fort and another town sitting like a mirror image across the Rio Grande. "That's Texas," Mr. Peacock-Hemlock-Jones said. "Brownsville, to be exact."

He left me to water the horses and refill our goatskin. There was no telling whether Mrs. Daggatt and General Dirty-Face Scurlock had already beat us to the treasure. We had lost considerable time.

I calculated Mr. Peacock-Hemlock-Jones would discover soon enough whether they had been seen in Matamoros, but he was gone an everlasting long time.

I sat in the shade and gazed across the muddy river at Texas. I had a yearning to set foot on the place, it was so close. A pole barge set out from Brownsville, ferrying over a wagon and horses, and I watched it to pass the time.

Mr. Peacock-Hemlock-Jones turned up with an old

shovel and a great bunch of carrots held in his fist like a bouquet.

"Provisions," he grinned. "An *artiste extraordinaire* never goes hungry. Our Boston friends have not been seen in Matamoros."

By that time I was on my feet and staring bug-eyed at the ferry halfway across the river. "Another five minutes, sir, and they will be. There she is! Big as a skinned ox! It's Mrs. Daggatt for certain, and General Scurlock, too!"

He flicked a glance across the water. "They do make an ugly pair, don't they? Nothing to worry about. We have a five-minute head start. Shall we go?"

It was true. Mr. Peacock-Hemlock-Jones had the scrimshaw map etched in his head. We followed the Rio Grande upriver all day, munching carrots, and he pointed out

landmarks I dimly recalled seeing on the whale's tooth. After a while, I stopped looking behind me. Mrs. Daggatt and General Scurlock most likely were taking their ease in Matamoros.

Late in the afternoon we saw a small town on the Texas side of the river and Mr. Peacock-Hemlock-Jones peered at it.

"Unless I miss my guess that dusty place calls itself Bent Elbow. You'll recall it was distinctly marked on the map."

I adjusted the *diklo* around my neck and felt the first real stirrings of excitement. The treasure hole couldn't be much further off. We might be weighted down with gold pieces before morning!

We crossed the shallow river and rode into town. It was a mortal dusty place. I made out Bodger's Barber Shop, a saloon, the jail, another saloon, Bodger's Hotel, two saloons, a bank, another saloon and Bodger's General Mercantile. And that was just one side of the street.

We dismounted in front of the hotel. Mr. Peacock-Hemlock-Jones addressed himself to a paunchy, small-eyed man sitting on a rickety chair in the shade of the porch. His polished boots were propped on the rail. "Is this Bent Elbow, Texas, sir?"

"Nope. You're lost, mister."

Mr. Peacock-Hemlock-Jones raised an eyebrow. "Impossible, sir. What do you call this place?"

"Crooked Elbow, Texas."

The man broke into a barking laugh, and the chair almost slipped out from under him. I sorely wished it had. Then he squinted at Billygoat and Sunflower and shook his head.

"You don't call those sorry-looking hay-burners *horses,* do you?"

"They're racehorses, to be exact," Mr. Peacock-Hemlock-Jones replied.

"*Race*horses. I do declare! I'm a racing man myself. Would a fifty-dollar purse interest you?"

"We never race for less than a hundred," Mr. Peacock-Hemlock-Jones stated firmly.

"A hundred it is, mister! You've got yourself a match. Two hundred would be more to my liking. Any distance, any conditions."

Mr. Peacock-Hemlock-Jones gazed at him with quiet scorn. "When we can spare a moment I'll look you up."

"I'll be waiting," the man barked. "Just ask for J.

Cooter Williams. You won't disappoint me, now, will you?"

"I wouldn't think of it," Mr. Peacock-Hemlock-Jones said, and we walked into the hotel.

He asked for the best accommodations, as if we already had our pockets full of treasure to spend. He registered with a flourish. Then, using the same pen, he made a perfect sketch of the scrimshaw ranch house, brick by brick, window by window, and he even drew in the bees and cattle.

He showed it to the hotel man, who turned out to be the leading citizen of Crooked Elbow, Texas — Mr. Bodger.

"Do you know this place, sir?"

Mr. Bodger was a round-faced man with sideburns like squirrel tails. "Appears to be Cactus John's old place," he said. "About three miles upriver. Nobody living there now, and nobody wants to."

"Why not?"

"The hornets are an unholy torment up around that bend in the river. They finally drove Cactus John out. I can't say folks around here were sorry to see him go. We kinda sided with the hornets."

"Not much daylight left," Mr. Peacock-Hemlock-Jones said. "Is there a lantern about you could spare us?"

"You'll find one hanging out back. Help yourself." Then he shifted expressions. "Did I hear J. Cooter Williams try to set you up to a horse race?"

"Exactly."

"He's never lost a race. You can't beat that filly of his."

Mr. Peacock-Hemlock-Jones nodded. "I appreciate your good advice, sir. But I've never lost a race, either."

Cactus John's place faced the river. Dark was coming on as we approached. The roof and stovepipe had fallen in and the adobe bricks had begun to melt away. Cottonwood trees had sprung up everywhere like weeds. I kept my ears tuned for hornets, but all I heard were jackrabbits shooting away through the underbrush.

A sagging pole fence meandered around the property and I recollected the scrimshaw carving of a longhorn steer tied to the northwest corner post. The way Mr. Peacock-Hemlock-Jones ciphered the map, that marked the spot to dig.

When we had found the post it had taken root and sprouted, and looked like a stunted tree.

"Hang up the lantern," Mr. Peacock-Hemlock-Jones said, and began to dig.

I looked on in feverish high spirits. The gold was certainly directly underfoot, but that post didn't want to come out. The roots had most likely taken a grip on the treasure itself. I took a spell at the shovel and after a moment Mr. Peacock-Hemlock-Jones remarked calmly, "Didn't you say your pa was a one-legged man?"

"Yes, sir," I replied.

"And his teeth were fairly rotted?"

"Black as tar," I murmured.

There was a long silence. Then he said, "A man an-

swering that description has been seen in Matamoros."

I gazed up at him in the lantern light. "When?"

"As recently as this morning."

My heart sank. I didn't want to think about it. I took a tighter grip on the shovel and began digging something fierce at the roots.

The post finally loosened like an old tooth. Together we lifted it out of the ground.

I fetched the lantern and we peered down into the post-hole. I expected to see a blaze of gold pieces.

But the hole was dark and empty.

Finally I said, "Maybe we didn't dig out the right post."

"No," he murmured. "We followed the scrimshaw map exactly."

He picked up the shovel and began deepening the hole. A small breeze rustled through the cottonwood trees. I thought about my pa thumping about Matamoros on his timber leg. I wished I were a thousand miles away.

Then, in the lantern light, I saw a mark carved in the old post. I lowered the lantern.

"Look," I said. "It's a *patrin!*"

He cast a glance at the post. Then he stepped closer and we both bent down to examine the mark.

"It is, indeed," he muttered.

I had never seen a gypsy sign exactly like it.

"Do you know what it means?" I asked.

He nodded. "It's the mark of a thief. In short, a warning to avoid this place."

"Do you think someone beat us to the treasure?" I muttered.

He shook his head. "The roots of that post haven't been disturbed. I'd better make inquiries about Mr. Cactus John. I suspect now that you were correct — we're not digging in the right place."

We started back for Crooked Elbow.

## 22

### THE HORNET'S NEST

Mr. Peacock-Hemlock-Jones left me at the hotel while he hunted up the sheriff, if there was one. I went up to bed and lay awake thinking of all the square miles stretching about where the treasure might be hidden. And I thought about my pa. I wondered if he had left that sign on the fence post. He was a gypsy, wasn't he? He'd know about *patrins*.

But I knew that I didnt want to go back to Matamoros and set eyes on him. I wasn't even certain now that Mr. Peacock-Hemlock-Jones had brought me along just to find him. Why did he need me to point out a one-legged man with black teeth? Men like that didn't exactly turn up by the bushel.

It was dreadful to consider that he meant to turn me over to my pa, and I kept putting that thought out my head. Mr. Peacock-Hemlock-Jones, was my friend, wasn't he? He wouldn't do a confounded thing like that.

When he woke me at dawn he was clearly in excellent spirits, and I said, "You found out where the treasure is hid! Did somebody move it?"

"On the contrary, Django. Somebody moved the fence post!"

We bolted down a full breakfast at the hotel and fetched the horses. J. Cooter Williams was once again sitting on the porch with his boots on the rail.

"Howdy," he said. "Got time for that horse race?"

"Make it noon today," Mr. Peacock-Hemlock-Jones said.

"What do you say to a $500 purse? Just to make it *interesting.*"

"Agreed, sir."

J. Cooter Williams broke into his barking laugh and we went plodding out of town. I disliked that man and wished we could win the race, but I knew Billygoat and Sunflower couldn't outrun a tumblebug. I calculated Mr. Peacock-Hemlock-Jones had let his anger get the best of his common sense.

We followed the river and arrived at Cactus John's place in about an hour. Now that it was daylight I was able to spot hornets' nests hanging like gray cabbages in the cottonwood trees. They made me downright uneasy. Mr. Peacock-Hemlock-Jones ignored them.

He walked here and there, getting his bearings. He squinted along one side of the fence and then along another side. Finally he counted out twenty paces back toward the ranch house, stopped, gazed about thoughtfully — and nodded.

"Throw me the shovel," he said, and began digging.

I kept an eye out for hornets, but after a while I began to think they were overrated. Gnats in the air were a good deal more troublesome. They came and went like drifts of black smoke.

Taking turns with the shovel, we soon had a hole big enough to bury a horse. "How do you know this is the right spot?" I asked. I was melting away in the heat.

"Because Cactus John was a thief. Keep digging. The treasure's bound to be close by."

I kept at it, enlarging the hole. We were well inside the fence and coming close to a cottonwood. I could see a hornet's nest dangling overhead, and it was worrisome.

Another ten minutes in that heat and I was no longer certain I cared to dig for treasure. The handle of the shovel was soaked with sweat.

And then I struck something. I yelled out and we both got down on our hands and knees and began scraping away the dirt.

In a minute or so we uncovered a pair of fat saddlebags. The leather was dry as paper, but it held together as we unbuckled the first sack and looked inside.

"Splendid," Mr. Peacock-Hemlock-Jones remarked.

"First rate and a half!" I declared.

The sack was gleaming with gold pieces. They shone in our faces like mirrors.

"Cactus John wasn't a common thief," Mr. Peacock-Hemlock-Jones grinned. "He was no doubt the meanest, *pettiest,* most astonishing *sneak* thief the West has ever known. He'd wait for the dark nights and then lift out his corner posts and move his fences. He was stealing land from his neighbors — a couple of feet at a time! That's what the sheriff told me. He swore it was true — you can see for yourself it was. I paced back to where the northwest corner post must have originally stood — the fool must have uncovered these saddlebags in the night without knowing it."

"And covered them over again!"

"Exactly. If your gypsy eye hadn't recognized that *patrin* we'd still be digging thirty feet off the mark. Now, let's get back to town. We've a race to run."

We began lifting the rotting bags carefully when a voice came rumbling through the air.

"That will do, gentlemen! Aye, and thank ye both for saving us the labor!"

General Scurlock halted twenty feet away, with a cocked pistol in his left hand. Beside him in the blazing sun stood Mrs. Daggatt, and she looked mad as a whole nest of hornets.

"You!" she bellowed. "You insolent little snip! You ungrateful offcast of creation! Is this the way you repay me for raising you up a little gentleman?"

"Yes, m'am," I said calmly.

"Trying to snatch away my treasure!"

"*Our* treasure, me dear Daggatt," General Scurlock said.

She kept her baggy, scowling eyes fixed on me. "Thought to cheat me of a few comforts in my old age, didn't you?"

"Yes, m'am," I answered, matching her scowl for scowl.

"Come, come, Daggatt," said General Scurlock. "Lost

treasure belongs to him what finds it. Or can get away with it, eh?" He turned to Mr. Peacock-Hemlock-Jones. "Now, sir, if you and the lad will kindly step clear I won't be obliged to use this pistol."

Mrs. Daggatt whipped a furious look at him. "Don't be more of a fool than usual. Can't you see it's them or us?"

"On the contrary, madam," said Mr. Peacock-Hemlock-Jones. "We are totally unarmed. The boy and I relinquish all claim. The treasure is yours. It was far more important business that brought us to the border."

General Scurlock gave a satisfied snort, but he kept the pistol leveled in our direction. We clambered out of the hole and they clambered in. Mrs. Daggatt was quick to lay open the gold, but the slow way her eyes took in the feast you'd think she was counting every piece.

"I believe you'll find it all there, madam," said Mr. Peacock-Hemlock-Jones.

General Scurlock chuckled and addressed himself to the problem of lifting the heavy saddlebags across his shoulder.

"Me dear Daggatt, I don't have three hands. If I can trust ye to hold the pistol I'm sure ye won't do anything rash."

Mr. Peacock-Hemlock-Jones and I exchanged quick glances. General Scurlock meant to see us dead, but a trace of military pride must have kept him from shooting unarmed men. He knew Mrs. Daggatt was not a woman to balk at anything. So did I.

She took the gun in her hand as if it were the treasure itself. Slowly I reached for the fetching stick in my hip pocket. As I watched her I saw a new and treacherous gleam spring into her eyes. The way she now gazed at General Scurlock I calculated she meant to use the pistol on *him* as well.

"Come along, *chavo*," Mr. Peacock-Hemlock-Jones murmured, as if to say the greater the distance the better the opportunity for Mrs. Daggatt to miss.

But I stood my ground, letting the string uncoil from my stick. As General Scurlock heaved the saddlebags over his shoulder I eyed a hornet's nest hanging directly above their heads.

In an instant I flicked out with the *kidda-kosh*. It whipped around the nest and I jerked back. The nest fell, split at their feet and a great roar of hornets erupted.

*Then* I ran. And so did Mrs. Daggatt. And so did General Scurlock, leaping madly toward the river.

When I glanced back Mrs. Daggatt had gone over the fence like a stampeding bull. And she kept going, with a cloud of hornets following along in an unholy temper.

Mr. Peacock-Hemlock-Jones yanked me off my feet and threw me into the underbrush. We lifted our heads and watched General Scurlock wading into the river. The rotting saddlebags had already begun to break apart and now gold pieces fell like leaves from his shoulder.

He stopped short, up to his knees in the river, and his arms going like a windmill to fend off the swarm. The saddlebags slipped from his shoulder. He was howling something fierce. I thought at first it was the hornets, but he appeared to be sinking in the mud.

"Daggatt! Daggatt!" he bellowed. "Quicksand!"

I raised myself a little higher. Mrs. Daggatt couldn't hear him. She was hopping about like a jackrabbit on the distant horizon. I looked back at the river.

"The gold's sinking away," I muttered.

"So is General Scurlock."

We watched for a while, until the swarm of hornets found more interesting business to attend to. Then we ventured closer. Mr. Peacock-Hemlock-Jones loosened a fence pole and held it out like a fishing rod.

"The gold's been sucked under!" he remarked. "That was very clumsy of you, General!"

General Scurlock's lumpy nose was swelling up and red as live coals. "Save me, sir! Haul me out!"

It was about as easy as hauling a hog out of a scalding tub. Finally he was sprawled and panting at the edge of

the river. A moment later he raised his head and gave us
a weak little smile.

"All that treasure quicksanded, eh? How deep do ye
reckon it'll sink?"

"Clear to China," Mr. Peacock-Hemlock-Jones replied.

# 23

## THE HORSE RACE

It was only when we mounted our horses that I realized I was hornet-stung, and so was Mr. Peacock-Hemlock-Jones. He had trouble sitting his horse and I watched him ease the torment as best he could.

"I'm dreadful sorry, sir," I said.

"Sorry? Why, you saved our lives with your *kidda-kosh*," he answered.

"But now the gold is lost!"

"We don't need it. Never did." And unaccountably he emptied out the goatskin of drinking water.

I gazed at him in stark wonderment. It seemed a buffle-brained thing to do, the day already afire, and I was not accustomed to Mr. Peacock-Hemlock-Jones doing buffle-brained things.

"You feverish again, sir?" I asked.

"Never felt better," he said, with a squint of pain. He slipped off his horse to walk the rest of the way. "But I must confess I'm not in proper shape for that confounded J. Cooter Williams. I'd be obliged, Django, if you'd run the competition for me."

I tugged at the green *diklo* knotted about my neck. "You're feverish for certain."

"What gives you that notion?"

"You poured out all our drinking water."

He nodded. "I did. In order to win the race."

By the time we reached Crooked Elbow my mouth was so dry I could have spit cotton. It was past noon, and the whole town seemed to have turned out for the occasion. I wished we would just keep moving. The only thing we were going to win in that race was a monstrous horse laugh.

Mr. Peacock-Hemlock-Jones led the way straight to the hotel. J. Cooter Williams watched us approach, guzzling beer in the shade of the porch. His polished boots were still propped on the rail. You'd think he was a hotel statue someone put out in the morning and took in at night.

"That man was born tired and brought up lazy," Mr. Peacock-Hemlock-Jones said. "I don't think he's well thought of. Look at the crowd watching us. Unless I miss my guess they'd like to see us beat him."

It was true. The faces along the boardwalks seemed uncommonly warm and friendly. But they didn't look especially hopeful. Just kind of sad about the whole thing.

"You're late," J. Cooter Williams smiled. "I was beginning to figure you were all talk and no horse race."

"You figured wrong," Mr. Peacock-Hemlock-Jones said.

J. Cooter Williams barked out a laugh and rose to his feet. "Then what are we waiting for? There's my filly

tied to the rail and rarin' to go. How far do you want to race?"

I gazed at the filly, a silky chestnut that had the look of harnessed lightning.

"Merely to the end of the street and back," said Mr. Peacock-Hemlock-Jones.

J. Cooter Williams' face sagged. "That ain't much of a race, mister."

"You'll find it long enough. As I recall, you said any distance and any conditions."

"I said it *then* and I say it *now*. Put up your money."

"One moment," Mr. Peacock-Hemlock-Jones remarked.

"That takes care of the distance. I'll hold you to two conditions."

"Take six," J. Cooter Williams laughed. "Why, both your horses together couldn't outrace a bull-maggot!" Then he pulled a heavy purse out of his shirt and tossed it to a loose-jointed man wearing the tallest hat I ever saw. "Sheriff, you hold the stakes. There's my five hundred cash dollars. Count 'em. I want this all done legal."

I came close to giving out a great sigh of relief. We couldn't race. We didn't have a cent to put up.

But I hadn't counted on Mr. Peacock-Hemlock-Jones. "Mr. Bodger," he called. "May we exchange a few private words with you."

The leading citizen of Crooked Elbow joined us between the horses, and you never heard such whispering.

"Wouldn't you like to dislodge Mr. J. Cooter Williams from your hotel porch, sir?"

"Indeed, I would," answered Mr. Bodger. "But he's too ornery to move on. Won't do a lick of work, except to keep his boots polished. Racing's his game."

"What would happen if we beat him in this contest, sir?"

"He'd be laughed out of town. Couldn't show his face."

"You're a man of property here in Crooked Elbow. A reversal in fortunes this morning has reduced us to an acute embarrassment of funds. We can't match Mr. William's purse. I'm asking you to put up the necessary stakes for us."

Mr. Bodger began to scratch through his squirrel tail

sideburns. "It's a terrible temptation, sir. But you can't beat his filly."

"There's always a first time, Mr. Bodger, and if you're any judge of character you can see that I'm not a fool."

There was a silence and then J. Cooter Williams called out impatiently. "We going to race horses or have a jawing match?"

Mr. Bodger glanced at the porch and tightened down one eye. "Cooter, I reckon you've met your match. Sheriff, is my word good enough for you? I'm backing these plow horses, five hundred dollars guaranteed."

J. Cooter Williams whipped his hat to the ground and almost laughed himself out of his boots.

"Mount your filly, Cooter," said the sheriff. Then he turned to Mr. Peacock-Hemlock-Jones. "Cooter has agreed to your conditions, sir, but I don't recall hearing what they was. Do you mind repeating them? We want everything legal-like."

By that time I was so thirsty I was gazing longingly at the water in the horse trough. But Mr. Peacock-Hemlock-Jones had firmly instructed me not to touch a drop of water.

"As I am unable to engage in equestrian competition," he said, "the boy here will substitute for me, riding my veteran racehorse, Sunflower. That's the *first* condition. Now let me see, gentlemen. The *second*. I counted five saloons along this side of the street and six on the other. At the shot of a pistol each rider will race to the first saloon, dismount, rush in, have a drink, rush out, mount up, ride to the next saloon, dismount, rush in, have a drink, rush out, mount up, ride to the next saloon, dismount, rush in, have a drink, rush out, mount up and continue in this manner. The first one to make it back, without missing a single saloon — wins the race."

"Agreed!" J. Cooter Williams roared, and began barking again. "Agreed! Agreed, sir!"

"The beverage will be milk."

The laugh strangled in J. Cooter Williams' throat. He turned chalky white. *"Milk!"*

"Certainly, sir," said Mr. Peacock-Hemlock-Jones. "I don't intend to have the boy served hard liquor."

I was perishing with thirst. I won the race by three saloons.

# 24

## THE MAN IN THE DARK

The last time I saw Mrs. Daggatt and General Dirty-Face Jim Scurlock they came straggling into town, leading their horses and wagon. They scuttled along, red as lobsters.

She was so hornet-stung and puffed up you could hardly see the eyes in her face. General Scurlock's nose had blossomed out like a ripe tomato. I think they would have snarled at each other, but I calculated it hurt too much.

"Howdy," Mr. Peacock-Hemlock-Jones said, tipping his straw hat to them. But they weren't feeling exactly social toward us and when they learned there was no doctor in town they kept moving. As far as I know they didn't stop until they reached Matamoros.

I spent a good part of the afternoon on the hotel porch with my buckskin boots propped on the rail. Once or twice I thought about the quicksand sucking down the saddlebag treasure deeper and deeper. It was enough to make a parson cuss, but Mr. Peacock-Hemlock-Jones had shrugged it off and I shrugged it off, too. I reckoned myself uncommon lucky. He had plucked me out of the orphan house and here we were more than two thousand miles away in Crooked Elbow, Texas.

When I thought of my pa it was only to hope that he would lead us an everlasting chase. Mr. Peacock-Hemlock-Jones and I would go on traveling the roads together. Maybe for years to come.

I felt mortal sorry for him, though. I had a hornet sting on my neck and three on my arms. But he had to eat his supper standing up.

I awoke in the night. Somewhere in my dreams I thought I heard the *thump-thud-thump* of a one-legged man approaching along the hall.

Now that I was awake I still heard it.

I sat up. The room was darker'n the inside of a wolf's mouth and I sensed that I was alone. The thumping drew nearer. It stopped outside the room. I'm certain I stopped breathing. The door opened silently and I broke into a fierce sweat.

The door closed and a man was standing in the room with me. I could hear him breathe and fancied I could almost see his black teeth.

"Don't come a step closer!" I said. "I know who you are. You're my pa!"

He didn't answer. He didn't move either. He just kept breathing in the dark.

"You followed us from Matamoros, didn't you?" I declared. "Well, don't think you're going to fetch me off with you!"

I could feel his eyes peering at me through the blackness.

"No, sir," I rattled on. "I won't go with you. I'm going with Mr. Peacock-Hemlock-Jones. You may be my pa, but he's my *friend*. And he'll be enormous mad if he catches you, sir!"

Not a sound from him.

"Enormous mad! I'm warning you, sir. Get!"

I could hear him shift his weight. He just let me talk and I was talking a blue streak. I couldn't help myself.

"You're no match for him!" I declared stoutly. "No man is — no sir! You'll do yourself a service by making a straight shirttail out of here. Why, he might walk in any second!"

But he wouldn't scare off. I could hear him rustling in his clothes. And then he struck a match.

It wasn't my pa. It was Mr. Peacock-Hemlock-Jones.

"I'm sorry I frightened you," he muttered, and lit the lamp.

He was carrying a heavy walking stick. I wiped the cold sweat from my face and gazed at him. His jaws were grimly set and his eyes avoided me.

"Mr. Bodger decided to outfit me with this mesquite stick," he said. "It's noisier than necessary, isn't it?"

"You might have said something," I answered. "I mistook you for my pa."

He turned slowly. He spoke in a voice so soft it barely carried. "I am your pa," he said.

I'm certain I didn't blink for a full minute. I wanted

to believe him, but I couldn't.

"My pa is a one-legged man," I said.

"No he isn't."

"He's a gypsy."

"No. I lived among gypsies. And I married a gypsy girl. Your mother was the most beautiful woman I ever painted. I tried for years to put her out of my mind, but I could paint her still."

The lamplight flickered about his face and cast a long, roving shadow across the walls. "After she died I wasn't myself for months on end. I thought I didn't want to be burdened with a child. I think now I wanted nothing about me to love, Django. Never again. Not even you. And I did a terrible thing. I told an old horse trader named Claudio to turn you over to the orphan house."

I gazed at him, but still his eyes avoided me.

"You were five years old. I'm aware of how terrifying it was for you. Claudio's stump leg froze itself in your mind. As the years went by you even blackened his teeth. I had discarded you. That was your way of discarding me."

I started to speak, but had to clear my throat. The few things I had always believed about my pa were false. The stories I had made up were closer to the truth. "Why didn't you tell me?" I muttered finally. "All these months traveling the roads, and you didn't tell me."

He stopped at the window and stood gazing into the darkness. "I was planning to wait until we got back to Matamoros. I had to be certain the time was right. I knew I had lost any claim to your regard. I wanted an opportunity to gain it back."

I stared at him. "Is that why you took me traveling?"

"Your scrimshaw map seemed the perfect excuse. We'd have a chance to get to know each other. If I were lucky, *chavo,* you might get to like me. You might even want to keep traveling the roads with me."

For the first time his eyes settled on me. But I turned away. He was my pa, and that changed everything.

We stayed in Crooked Elbow another day. I kept to myself. I had to rethink all my thoughts. I had spent all the years I could remember thinking of my pa one way and I wasn't certain I could ever think of him another. Mr. Bodger saw that something was bothering me and took it upon himself to cheer me up by talking about the weather.

"Awful hot in these parts, wouldn't you say, lad? But healthy. Awful healthy. Folks live forever around here. Why, we had to shoot a man to start a cemetery."

And then we left, heading back for Matamoros.

"That horse race money is yours," Mr. Peacock-Hemlock-Jones said. "You're about old enough to make your own way, if that's what you want."

It must have been an hour before I replied. "What does a *vardo* cost?"

"I don't think there are any gypsy-style wagons to be had in Matamoros. It would have to be special-made and carved by an expert and painted by an artist."

"You're an *artiste extraordinaire.*"

"Indeed I am. It's an idea."

"A splendid idea," I said.

"First rate," he smiled.

"First rate and a half," I smiled.

"By thunder, we'll do it!" he laughed.

"Indeed we will!" I laughed.

"The fanciest, brightest gypsy wagon ever drawn by two racehorses!" my father roared.